Lyrics & Chords
90 Acoustic Hits

Published by
WISE PUBLICATIONS
14-15 Berners Street, London W1T 3LJ, UK.

Exclusive Distributors:
MUSIC SALES LIMITED
Distribution Centre, Newmarket Road,
Bury St Edmunds, Suffolk IP33 3YB, UK.
MUSIC SALES PTY LIMITED
Music Sales Pty Limited
20 Resolution Drive, Caringbah, NSW 2229, Australia.

Order No. AM1001385
ISBN 978-1-84938-664-7
This book © Copyright 2010 Wise Publications,
a division of Music Sales Limited.

Music arranged by Matt Cowe.
Music edited by Adrian Hopkins.
Compiled by Nick Crispin.
Music processed by Paul Ewers Music Design.

Cover photo, pages 62, 76, 89, 179, 209 courtesy of LFI.
Page 16 Jim Dyson/Getty Images,
page 129 Lex Van Rossen/Getty Images,
page 32 Jon Super/Redferns,
page 45 Steve Jennings/Wire Image,
page 154 Jason Merritt/Film Magic.

Printed in the EU.

Your Guarantee of Quality
As publishers, we strive to produce every book to the
highest commercial standards. This book has been carefully
designed to minimise awkward page turns and to make
playing from it a real pleasure. Particular care has been
given to specifying acid-free, neutral-sized paper made from pulps
which have not been elemental chlorine bleached. This pulp is from
farmed sustainable forests and was produced with special regard
for the environment. Throughout, the printing and binding have
been planned to ensure a sturdy, attractive publication which
should give years of enjoyment. If your copy fails to meet our high
standards, please inform us and we will gladly replace it.

www.musicsales.com

WISE PUBLICATIONS
PART OF THE MUSIC SALES GROUP
LONDON / NEW YORK / PARIS / SYDNEY / COPENHAGEN / BERLIN / MADRID / TOKYO

Contents

Acts Of Man

Words & Music by
Tim Smith

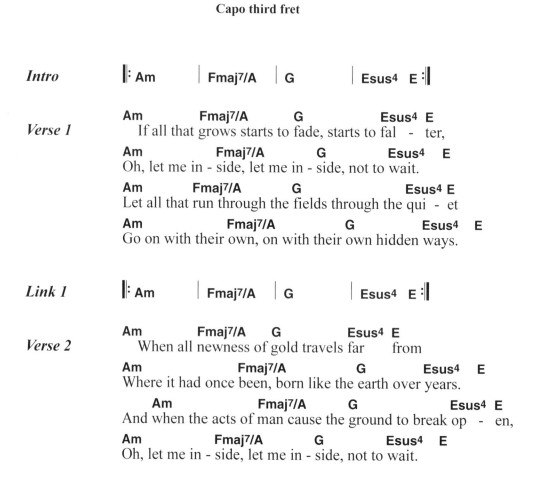

Capo third fret

Intro   ‖: Am | Fmaj7/A | G | Esus4 E :‖

Verse 1

Am   Fmaj7/A   G   Esus4 E
  If all that grows starts to fade, starts to fal - ter,

Am   Fmaj7/A   G   Esus4   E
Oh, let me in - side, let me in - side, not to wait.

Am   Fmaj7/A   G   Esus4 E
Let all that run through the fields through the qui - et

Am   Fmaj7/A   G   Esus4   E
Go on with their own, on with their own hidden ways.

Link 1   ‖: Am | Fmaj7/A | G | Esus4 E :‖

Verse 2

Am   Fmaj7/A   G   Esus4 E
  When all newness of gold travels far   from

Am   Fmaj7/A   G   Esus4   E
Where it had once been, born like the earth over years.

   Am   Fmaj7/A   G   Esus4 E
And when the acts of man cause the ground to break op - en,

Am   Fmaj7/A   G   Esus4   E
Oh, let me in - side, let me in - side, not to wait.

Chorus 1

Am   F   G   C
Great are the sounds of all that live
     F   E
And all that man can hold.

Instrumental

‖: Am | F | G | C |
| F | F | E   :‖

Verse 3

Am   Fmaj7/A   G   Esus4 E
  If all that grows starts to fade, starts to fal - ter,
Am   Fmaj7/A   G   Esus4   E
Oh, let me in - side, let me in - side, not to wait.

Chorus 2

Am   F   G   C
Great are the sounds of all that live
     F   E
And all that man can hold.
Am   F   G   C   F   E Am
Great are the sounds of all that live, that live.

Becoming A Jackal

Words & Music by
Conor J. O'Brien

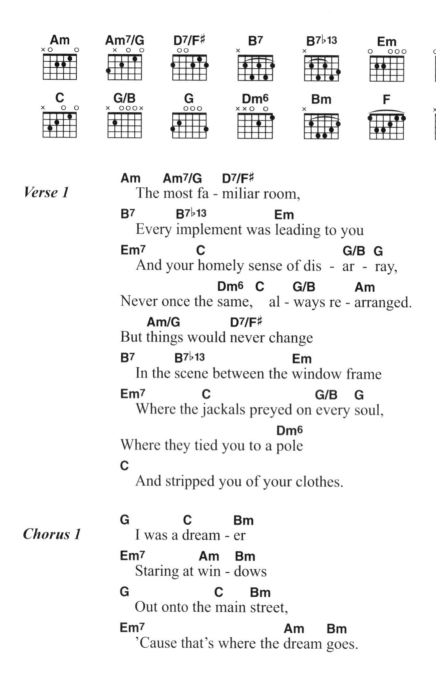

Verse 1

Am   Am7/G D7/F♯
The most fa - miliar room,

B7   B7♭13   Em
Every implement was leading to you

Em7   C   G/B G
And your homely sense of dis - ar - ray,

              Dm6 C   G/B   Am
Never once the same,   al - ways re - arranged.

      Am/G   D7/F♯
But things would never change

B7   B7♭13   Em
In the scene between the window frame

Em7   C   G/B   G
Where the jackals preyed on every soul,

                  Dm6
Where they tied you to a pole

C
And stripped you of your clothes.

Chorus 1

G   C   Bm
I was a dream - er

Em7   Am Bm
Staring at win - dows

G   C   Bm
Out onto the main street,

Em7   Am   Bm
'Cause that's where the dream goes.

Verse 2

    C   G/B Am   Am7/G D7/F♯
And each time they found   fresh meat to chew,

B7   B7♭13   Em
  I would turn away and return to you.

Em7   C   G/B   G
  You would offer me your un - made bed

                Dm6 C   G/B   Am
Feed me till I'm fed   and read me till I'm read.

      Am/G   D7/F♯
But when the morning came,

B7   B7♭13   Em
  You would catch me at the window again

Em7   C   G/B   G
  In an eyes wide open sleep - ing   state

            Dm6 C   (G)
Staring into space   with no look upon my face.

Chorus 2   As Chorus 1

Bridge

C   G   Am   Am7/G
  And when I got older,   when I grew bolder,

F   G   Am G/B Am
  Out onto the streets I flew.

               G/B
Released from your shackles

C   Dm   Em F
  I danced with the jack - als

                   Em
And learned a new way to move.

Verse 3

        Am   D7/F♯
So be - fore you take this song as truth,

B7   Em
  You should wonder what I'm taking from you,

     C   G
How I benefit from you being here,

          Dm6 C   (G)
Lending me your ears   while I'm selling you my fears.

Chorus 3

G   C   Bm   Em
  I was a dream - er, (I'm selling you my fears)

                 Am Bm   G
Staring at win - dows, (I'm selling you my fears)

               C   Bm   Em
Out onto the main street, (I'm selling you my fears)

                     Am   Bm
'Cause that's where the dream goes. (I'm selling you)

G   C   Bm
  I was a dream - er

Em   Am Bm
  Staring at win - dows

G   C   Bm
  Out onto the main street,

Em   Am   Bm
  'Cause that's where the dream goes.

Better Together

Words & Music by
Jack Johnson

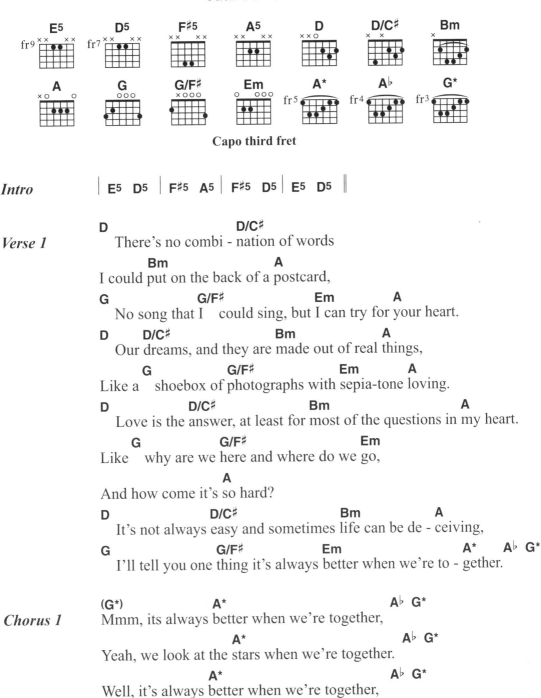

Capo third fret

Intro   ‖ E5   D5 │ F♯5   A5 │ F♯5   D5 │ E5   D5 ‖

Verse 1

D   D/C♯
There's no combi - nation of words
    Bm   A
I could put on the back of a postcard,
G   G/F♯   Em   A
  No song that I   could sing, but I can try for your heart.
D   D/C♯   Bm   A
  Our dreams, and they are made out of real things,
    G   G/F♯   Em   A
Like a   shoebox of photographs with sepia-tone loving.
D   D/C♯   Bm   A
  Love is the answer, at least for most of the questions in my heart.
    G   G/F♯   Em
Like   why are we here and where do we go,
                      A
And how come it's so hard?
D   D/C♯   Bm   A
  It's not always easy and sometimes life can be de - ceiving,
G   G/F♯   Em   A*   A♭ G*
  I'll tell you one thing it's always better when we're to - gether.

Chorus 1

(G*)   A*   A♭ G*
Mmm, its always better when we're together,
                          A*   A♭ G*
Yeah, we look at the stars when we're together.
                      A*   A♭ G*
Well, it's always better when we're together,
                      A*
Yeah, it's always better when we're together.

Link 1 ‖: D D/C♯ | Bm A | G G/F♯ | Em A* :‖

Verse 2

(A*)   D   D/C♯
And all of these moments just might find their way
       Bm   A
Into my dreams to - night,
       G   G/F♯
But I know that they'll be gone
            Em   A   D
When the morning light sings and brings new things.
D/C♯   Bm   A
     For to - morrow night you see
       G   G/F♯   Em   A
That they'll be gone too, too many things I have to do.
                       D   D/C♯
But if all of these dreams might find their way
       Bm   A
Into my day to day scene,
       G   G/F♯   Em   A
I'd be under the impres - sion I was somewhere in be - tween.
            D   D/C♯   Bm   A
With only two just me and you, not so many things we got to do,
     G   G/F♯
Or places we got to be,
            Em   A*   A♭ G*
We'll sit be - neath the mango tree now.

Chorus 2

(G*)   A*   A♭ G*
Yeah, it's always better when we're together,
                            A*   A♭ G*
Mmm, we're somewhere in between together.
                  A*   A♭ G*
Well, it's always better when we're together,
                  A*
Yeah, it's always better when we're together.

Link 2

D   D/C♯   Bm   A
Mmm, mmm, mm, mm, mm, mm, mm, mm.
G   G/F♯   Em   A
  Mm, mm, mm, mm, mmm, mmm, mm, mm.

| D D/C♯ | Bm A | G G/F♯ | Em A ‖

10

Bridge

Em   A*   Em
   I believe in memo - ries, they look so,

                  A*   Em
So pretty when I sleep. Hey now and,

           A*
And when I wake up,

           Em   A*
You look so pretty sleeping next to me.

        G*   A*
But there is   not enough time,

           G*   A*
And there is no,   no song I could sing,

           G*   A*
And there is no   combination of words I could say,

       G*   A*
But I will still tell you one thing we're better together.

Outro   ‖: D D/C♯ | Bm A | G G/F♯ | Em A* :‖ D   ‖

Blood Bank

Words & Music by
Justin Vernon

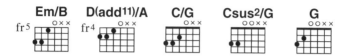

Intro

Em/B D(add¹¹)/A C/G Csus²/G C/G
Ooh._____

Em/B D(add¹¹)/A C/G Csus²/G C/G
Ooh._____

Em/B D(add¹¹)/A C/G Csus²/G C/G
Ooh._____

Em/B D(add¹¹)/A C/G Csus²/G C/G
Ooh._____

Verse 1

(C/G) **Em/B**   **D(add¹¹)/A**
Well I met you at the blood bank,

        C/G
We were looking at the bags.

                    Em/B   **D(add¹¹)/A**
Wondering if any of the colours

              C/G
Matched any of the names we knew on the tags.

            G
You said see look at that's yours

        D(add¹¹)/A
Stacked on top with your brothers.

                Em/B
See how they re - semble one another's

            C/G
Even in their plastic little covers?

Chorus 1

C/G   **Em/B D(add¹¹)/A**
And I said I know it well,

        C/G
That secret that you know

              D(add¹¹)/A
That you don't know how to tell.

cont.

        G
It fucks with your honour
        D(add11)/A
And it teases your head.
        Em/B
But you know that it's good girl,
          Csus2/G
'Cause it's running you with red.

Verse 2

N.C.   **Em/B**   **D(add11)/A**
Then the snow started falling,
           C/G   **Csus2/G**
We were stuck out in your car.
        Em/B   **D(add11)/A**
You were rubbing both my hands,
        C/G
Chewing on a candy bar.
             G
You said ain't this just like the present,
        D(add11)/A
To be showing up like this.
        Em/B
There's a moon waning crescent,
      C/G   **Csus2/G** **C/G**
We started to kiss.

Chorus 2

C/G   **Em/B** **D(add11)/A**
And I said I know it well,
      C/G
That secret that we know,
          D(add11)/A
That we don't know how to tell.
     G
I'm in love with your honour,
        D(add11)/A
I'm in love with your cheeks.
         Em/B
What's that noise up the stairs baby,
        C/G
Is that Christmas morning calling?

Outro

C/G   **Em/B** **D(add11)/A**
And I know it well.
        C/G   **Em/B** **D(add11)/A**
:|| And I know it well. ||: *Play 7 times*

Blue Skies

Words & Music by
Charlie Fink

C **Csus2** **Csus4** **F** **C5** **Dm** **Fadd9** **C6/B♭**

⑥ = C   ③ = F
⑤ = G   ② = A
④ = C   ① = D

Intro
‖: C Csus2 Csus4 Csus2 | C Csus2 Csus4 Csus2 | F | F :‖

Verse 1

C5
This is a song for anyone with a bro - ken heart. F

C5
This is a song for anyone who can't get out of bed. F

Dm   C5
I'll do anything to be happy,

Dm   F   C5
Oh, 'cause blue skies are calling,   but I know that it's hard.

Link
‖: C   Csus2 C5 Csus2 | C   Csus2 C5 Csus2 | F | F :‖

Verse 2

C5   Dm   F
This is the last song that I write while still in love with you.

C5   Dm   F
    This is the last song that I write while you're even on   my mind.

Dm   C5
'Cause it's time to leave those feelings be - hind,

Dm   F   C5
Oh, 'cause blue skies are coming,   but I know that it's   hard.

Bridge

Fadd9
I don't think that it's the end,
    C6/B♭   **Fadd9**
But I know we can't keep going.

I don't think that it's the end,
    C6/B♭   **Fadd9**
But I know we can't keep going.
  Dm   **G**
But blue skies are calling,
        Dm   **G**
Oh yeah, blue skies are calling,
        Dm   **G**
Oh yeah, blue skies are coming,
               C5
But I know that it's hard.

Outro

‖: **C** **Csus2** **Csus4** **Csus2** | **C** **Csus2** **Csus4** **Csus2** | **F** | **F** :‖

Play 4 times

| **C5** ‖

Nick Cave

Breathless

Words & Music by
Nick Cave

Intro

C	G	C	G
F	G	C	G
C	G	F	G

Verse 1

```
        C              G                      C
    It's up in the morning it's on the downs
                      G                    F
And little white clouds like gambolling lambs
            G        C
And I am breathless over you
                      G             C
And the red-breasted robin beats his wings
            G            F
His throat it trembles when he sings
            G        C
For he is helpless before you
                      G
And the happy hooded bluebells bow
            C        G            F
And they bend their heads all a-down
            G                  C
Heavied by the early morning dew
                  G                    C
At the whispering stream, at the bubbling brook
            G        F
The fishes leap up to take a look
            G        C
For they are breathless over you
```

cont.

            G
Still your hands
                 C
And still your heart
             G   **F**
For still your face comes shining through
            G   **C**
And all the morning glows a - new
            G
Still your mind
            C
Still your soul
            G   **F**
For still, the fire of love is true
           G   **(C)**
And I am breathless without you

Instrumental | **C** | **F G** | **C** | **F G** ‖

Verse 2
   C   **G**
   The wind circles a - mong the trees
        C   **G**   **F**
And it bangs about the new-made leaves
        G   **C**
For it is breathless without you
              G
And the fox chases the rabbit round
        C   **G**   **F**
And the rabbit hides be - neath the ground
        G   **C**
For he is defenceless without you
           G
The sky of day - time dies away
       C   **G**   **F**
And all the earthly things they stop to play
        G   **C**
For we are all breathless without you
        G
I listen to my juddering bones
       C   **G**   **F**
And the blood in my veins, the wind in my lungs
        G   **C**
And I am breathless without you

cont.

        G
Still your hands

           C
And still your heart

          G   F
For still your face comes shining through

         G   C
And all the morning glows a - new

        G
Still your soul

        C
Still your mind

         G   F
For still, the fire of love is true

        G   F   C
And I am breathless without you

Carol Brown

Words & Music by
Jemaine Clement & Bret McKenzie

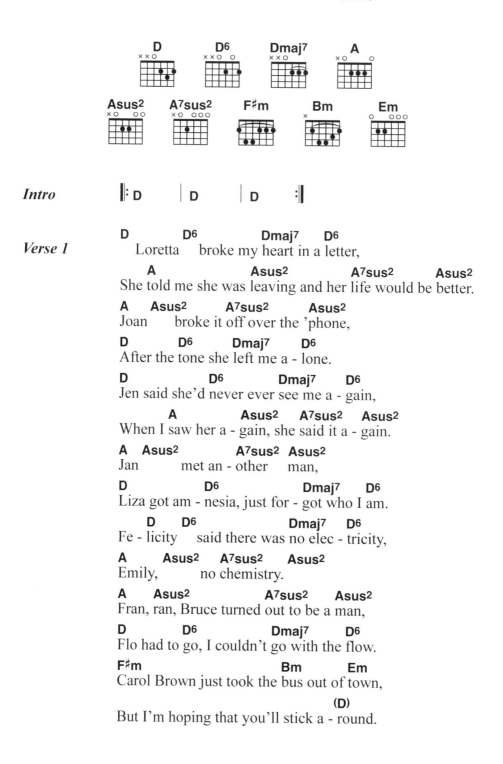

Intro   ‖: D ‖ D ‖ D :‖

Verse 1

D   D6   Dmaj7 D6
Loretta   broke my heart in a letter,

    A   Asus2   A7sus2   Asus2
She told me she was leaving and her life would be better.

A Asus2   A7sus2   Asus2
Joan   broke it off over the 'phone,

D   D6   Dmaj7   D6
After the tone she left me a - lone.

D   D6   Dmaj7   D6
Jen said she'd never ever see me a - gain,

       A   Asus2 A7sus2 Asus2
When I saw her a - gain, she said it a - gain.

A Asus2   A7sus2 Asus2
Jan   met an - other   man,

D   D6   Dmaj7   D6
Liza got am - nesia, just for - got who I am.

      D   D6   Dmaj7   D6
Fe - licity   said there was no elec - tricity,

A   Asus2 A7sus2   Asus2
Emily,   no chemistry.

A   Asus2   A7sus2   Asus2
Fran, ran, Bruce turned out to be a man,

D   D6   Dmaj7   D6
Flo had to go, I couldn't go with the flow.

F#m   Bm   Em
Carol Brown just took the bus out of town,

                           (D)
But I'm hoping that you'll stick a - round.

Link 1 | D | D | D | D ‖

Bridge 1

Em   D   A
   (He doesn't cook or clean, he's not good boyfriend ma - terial.)
                   Em
Ooh, we can eat cereal.

                                          D   A
(You'll lose interest fast, his re - lationships never last.)
                   Em
Shut up girlfriends from the past.

                                                D   A
(He says he'll do one thing and then he goes and does an - other thing.)
         Em   D
Oh,___ who organised all of my ex-girlfriends into a choir
                   A
And got them to sing?
Em
   (Ah.)

              D A   Em
Ooh, ooh,   mmm, shut up,
         D A
(Ah.)_____

                                          (D)
Shut up girlfriends from the past.

Link 2 | D | D | D | D ‖

Verse 2

D   D6   Dmaj7   D6
Mimi   will no longer see me,

A   Asus2   A7sus2 Asus2
Brittany,   Brittany hit me.

A   Asus2   A7sus2   Asus2
Paula, Per - sephone, Stella, and Stephanie,

              D   D6   Dmaj7   D6
There must be fifty ways that lovers have left me.

F♯m   Bm   Em
Carol Brown just took the bus out of town.

Em   D   A

Love is a delicate thing, you can't just throw it away on the breeze.

                        Em

(He said the same thing to me.)

                                    D   A

How can we ever know if I'm the right person in this world?

                               Em

(He means he looks at other girls.)

                          D   A

Love is a mystery, it does not follow rules.

                      Em

(This guy is a fool,)

                                    D   A

(He'll always be a boy, he's a man who never grew up.)

                                Em

I thought I told you to shut up.

(Ah.)

D   A

Mona, you told me you were in a coma.

Em

  (Ah.)

D   A

Tiffany, you said that you had an epiphany.

Em   D   A

  Mmm, would you like a little cere - al?

Em

  Who organised this choir of ex-girlfriends

                 D   A

Was it you Carol Brown, was it you Carol Brown?

F♯m   Bm   Em

Carol Brown just took a bus out of town,

                                (D)

But I'm hoping that you'll stick a - round.

D

Outro   Stick around. (Do do do do do do do do do.)

Stick around. (Do do do do do do.)

Do do do do do, stick around.

Do do do do do, stick around.

The Cave

Words & Music by
Mumford & Sons

C#m7   E/B   G#5   E   A(add9)/E   B   C#m7*   A

⑥ = D   ③ = F#
⑤ = A   ② = A
④ = D   ① = D

Capo second fret

Intro

| C#m7 | E/B | C#m7 | E/B | |

| C#m7 | E/B G#5 | E A(add9)/E | E | |

Verse 1

(E)   C#m7   E/B
It's empty in the valley of your heart,

                        C#m7   E/B
The sun, it rises slowly as you walk

                        C#m7
Away from all the fears

                E/B   G#5   E   A(add9)/E E
And all the faults you've left be - hind.

                        C#m7   E/B
The harvest left no food for you to eat,

                        C#m7   E/B
You cannibal, you meat-eater, you see.

                        C#m7
But I have seen the same,

                E/B   G#5   E   A(add9)/E E
I know the shame in your de - feat.

Chorus 1

E   A(add9)/E E
But I will hold on   hope

                A(add9)/E E
And I won't let you   choke

A(add9)/E E   B
On   the   noose a - round your neck.

cont.

      C♯m7   A   E
And I'll find strength in pain

      C♯m7 A   E
And I will change my ways,

    A   E   B
I'll know my name as it's called again.

Link 1

| C♯m7 | E/B | C♯m7 | E/B |

| C♯m7 | E/B   G♯5 | E   A(add9)/E | E   ‖

Verse 2

(E)   C♯m7   E/B
'Cause I have other things to fill my time,

              C♯m7   E/B
You take what is yours and I'll take mine.

              C♯m7
Now let me at the truth

             E/B   G♯5   E   A(add9)/E E
Which will re - fresh my broken mind.

            C♯m7   E/B
So tie me to a post and block my ears,

               C♯m7   E/B
I can see widows and orphans through my tears.

             C♯m7
I know my call de - spite my faults

      E/B   G♯5   E   A(add9)/E E
And de - spite my growing fears.

Chorus 2   As Chorus 1

Verse 3

(E)   C♯m7   E/B
So come out of your cave walking on your hands

             C♯m7   E/B
And see the world hanging upside down.

               C♯m7
You can understand de - pendence

      E/B   G♯5   E   A(add9)/E E
When you know the maker's land.

Chorus 3

      E   A(add9)/E E
So make your siren's   call

        E   A(add9)/E E
And sing all you   want,

     A(add9)/E E   B
I will not   hear what you have to say.

        C♯m7* A   E
'Cause I need freedom now

        C♯m7* A   E
And I need to know how

     A   E   B
To live my life as it's meant to be.

Instrumental ‖: E | A   E | E | A   E | A   E | B   :‖

Chorus 4

      E   A(add9)/E E
And I will hold on   hope

              A(add9)/E E
And I won't let you   choke

A(add9)/E E   B
On   the   noose a - round your neck.

       C♯m7*   A   E
And I'll find strength in pain

       C♯m7* A   E
And I will   change my ways,

     A   E   B   E
I'll know my name as it's called again.

Cell Mates

Words & Music by
Matt Caughthran & William Malpede

G   C   D   B7   Em

Intro

| G | G ‖

‖: G | G | G | G | C D | G | G :‖

Verse 1

G
In my defence these prison walls,
                  C   D   G
They couldn't hold any - thing in at all.

I see your face in my own walls,
                C   D   C
And I keep crawling on back to you.

Chorus 1

C B7 Em   D C   G   D
       Honest - ly, will you wait for me?
  C   B7   Em   D C   G   D
A little word, promise me one day I'll be free.

Link 1

| G | G | G | G |

| G | G | C D | G | G ‖

Verse 2

G
This kind of place, it brings you down,
                    C   D   G
Everyone's dragging their feet on the ground.

Your kind of face could save a soul,
                    C   D   C
It keeps me crying on out to you.

Chorus 2   As Chorus 1

Instrumental ‖: G | G | G | G |

              | D | D | D | D   :‖

             C B7 Em   D C   G   D
Chorus 3   Honest - ly, will you wait for me?
               C   B7   Em   D C   G   D
A little word, promise me one day I'll be free.

I'll be free, I'll be free, I'll be free.

Outro | G | G | G | G | G | G   ‖

                   C   D   G
I keep on crawling on back to you.

Charlie Darwin

Words & Music by
Benjamin Knox Miller, Jeffrey Prystowsky & Jocelyn Adams

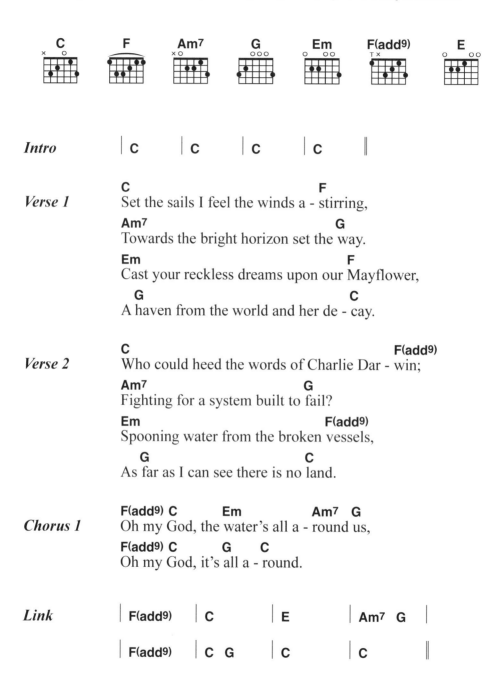

Intro
| C | C | C | C |

Verse 1
C   F
Set the sails I feel the winds a - stirring,
Am⁷   G
Towards the bright horizon set the way.
Em   F
Cast your reckless dreams upon our Mayflower,
   G   C
A haven from the world and her de - cay.

Verse 2
C   F(add⁹)
Who could heed the words of Charlie Dar - win;
Am⁷   G
Fighting for a system built to fail?
Em   F(add⁹)
Spooning water from the broken vessels,
   G   C
As far as I can see there is no land.

Chorus 1
F(add⁹) C   Em   Am⁷ G
Oh my God, the water's all a - round us,
F(add⁹) C   G   C
Oh my God, it's all a - round.

Link
| F(add⁹) | C | E | Am⁷ G |
| F(add⁹) | C G | C | C |

Verse 3

C   F(add9)
Who could heed the words of Charlie Dar - win?

Am7   G
Lords of war just profit from de - cay

          Em   F(add9)
And trade the children's promise for the jingle,

        G   C
The way we trade our hard earned time for pay.

Chorus 2

F(add9) C   E   Am7   G
Oh my God, the water's cold and shape - less,

F(add9) C   G   C
Oh my God, it's all a - round.

F(add9) C   E   Am7   G
Oh my God, life is cold and form - less,

F(add9) C   G   C
Oh my God, it's all a - round.

Outro

| F(add9) | C | E | Am7 G |
| F(add9) | C G | C | C F(add9) | C ‖

Chasing Cars

Words & Music by
Gary Lightbody, Nathan Connolly, Tom Simpson,
Paul Wilson & Jonathan Quinn

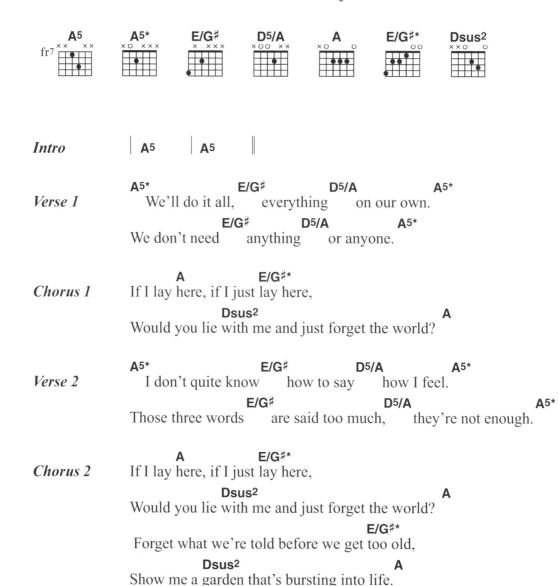

Intro | A5 | A5 ||

Verse 1
A5*   E/G♯   D5/A   A5*
We'll do it all,   everything   on our own.
                E/G♯   D5/A   A5*
We don't need   anything   or anyone.

Chorus 1
            A   E/G♯*
If I lay here, if I just lay here,
           Dsus2   A
Would you lie with me and just forget the world?

Verse 2
A5*   E/G♯   D5/A   A5*
I don't quite know   how to say   how I feel.
                E/G♯   D5/A   A5*
Those three words   are said too much,   they're not enough.

Chorus 2
            A   E/G♯*
If I lay here, if I just lay here,
           Dsus2   A
Would you lie with me and just forget the world?
                              E/G♯*
Forget what we're told before we get too old,
           Dsus2   A
Show me a garden that's bursting into life.

Verse 3

   A5*   **E/G♯**   **D5/A**   **A5***
Let's waste time   chasing cars   around our heads.

          E/G♯   **D5/A**   **A5***
I need your grace   to remind me   to find my own.

Chorus 3

       A   **E/G♯***
If I lay here, if I just lay here,

        Dsus2   **A**
Would you lie with me and just forget the world?

                    E/G♯*
Forget what we're told before we get too old,

       Dsus2   **A**
Show me a garden that's bursting into life.

Bridge 1

            E/G♯*
All that I am, all that I ever was

       Dsus2   **A**
Is here in your perfect eyes, they're all I can see.

                E/G♯*
I don't know where, confused about how as well,

         Dsus2   **A**
Just know that these things will never change for us at all.

Chorus 4

      A5*   **E/G♯**
If I lay here, if I just lay here,

      D5/A   **A5***
Would you lie with me and just forget the world?

Bonnie 'Prince' Billy

Cursed Sleep

Words & Music by
Will Oldham

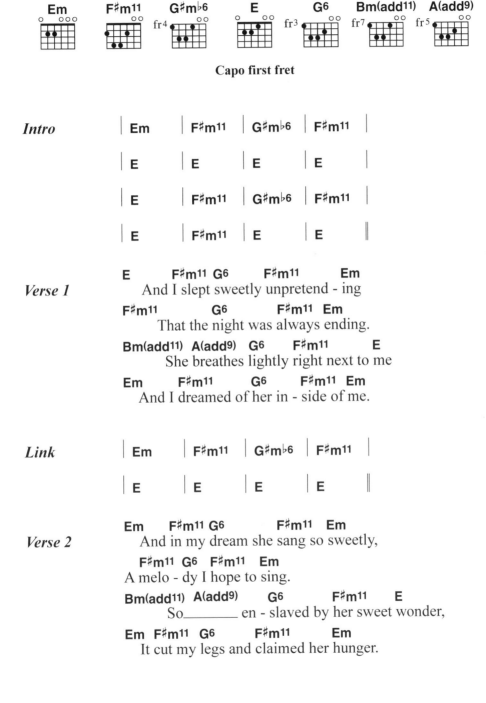

Capo first fret

Intro

| Em | F♯m11 | G♯m♭6 | F♯m11 |

| E | E | E | E |

| E | F♯m11 | G♯m♭6 | F♯m11 |

| E | F♯m11 | E | E |

Verse 1

E   F♯m11 G6   F♯m11   Em
And I slept sweetly unpretend - ing

F♯m11   G6   F♯m11 Em
    That the night was always ending.

Bm(add11) A(add9) G6   F♯m11   E
    She breathes lightly right next to me

Em   F♯m11   G6   F♯m11 Em
And I dreamed of her in - side of me.

Link

| Em | F♯m11 | G♯m♭6 | F♯m11 |

| E | E | E | E |

Verse 2

Em   F♯m11 G6   F♯m11   Em
And in my dream she sang so sweetly,

F♯m11 G6 F♯m11   Em
A melo - dy I hope to sing.

Bm(add11) A(add9)   G6   F♯m11   E
    So_____ en - slaved by her sweet wonder,

Em F♯m11 G6   F♯m11   Em
It cut my legs and claimed her hunger.

Verse 3

E   F♯m¹¹   G⁶   F♯m¹¹ Em
She sang my name and so en - gulfed,

     F♯m¹¹   G⁶ F♯m¹¹   Em
And I cried and felt my legs fail.

Bm(add¹¹) A(add⁹) G⁶   F♯m¹¹   E
   In her   arms I trembled e - lectric

Em   F♯m¹¹ G⁶   F♯m¹¹ Em
Oh, and she led me and she held me.

Instrumental 1

Em	F♯m¹¹	G♯m♭6	F♯m¹¹
E	E	E	E
Em	F♯m¹¹	G♯m♭6	F♯m¹¹
E	E	E	E
Bm(add¹¹)	A(add⁹)	G⁶	F♯m¹¹
E	E	E	E
E	Em	Em	Em ‖

Verse 4

Em   F♯m¹¹ G⁶   F♯m¹¹ Em
Then waking she was older still,

     F♯m¹¹   G⁶   F♯m¹¹   Em
And holds my love a - gainst its will.

Bm(add¹¹) A(add⁹) G⁶   F♯m¹¹   E
   In spell   cast with her palms ex - tended,

Em F♯m¹¹ G⁶   F♯m¹¹ Em
Cursed love is never ended.

Bridge

Bm(add¹¹)   A(add⁹) G⁶   F♯m¹¹ E
  Cur - sed   eyes are never closing,

Bm(add¹¹)   A(add⁹) G⁶   F♯m¹¹ E
  Cur - sed   arms are never closing.

Bm(add¹¹)   A(add⁹) G⁶   F♯m¹¹E
  Cur - sed   children never rising,

Em   F♯m¹¹ G⁶   F♯m¹¹ Em
 Cur - sed   me nev - er des - pising.

Instrumental 2 | **Em** | **F♯m¹¹** | **G♯m♭⁶** | **F♯m¹¹** |

| **E** | **E** | **E** | **E** |

| **Em** | **F♯m¹¹** | **G♯m♭⁶** | **F♯m¹¹** |

| **E** | **E** | **E** | **E** ‖

Verse 5

E   F♯m¹¹ G⁶   F♯m¹¹ Em
Oh, I am   loving, always holding,

F♯m¹¹ G⁶   F♯m¹¹   Em
Well, she   sleeps, her song en - folding.

Bm(add¹¹) A(add⁹) G⁶   F♯m¹¹ E
E - pic   song it tells of how,

Em F♯m¹¹ G⁶ F♯m¹¹   Em
Of she and I are   living now.

Outro

Bm(add¹¹) A(add⁹) G⁶   F♯m¹¹ E
                        Cursed love.

Bm(add¹¹) A(add⁹) G⁶   F♯m¹¹ E
                        Cursed love.

Bm(add¹¹) A(add⁹) G⁶   F♯m¹¹ Em   E
                        Cursed love.

Bm(add¹¹) A(add⁹) G⁶   F♯m¹¹ E

Dear God (Sincerely M.O.F.)

Words & Music by
Jim James

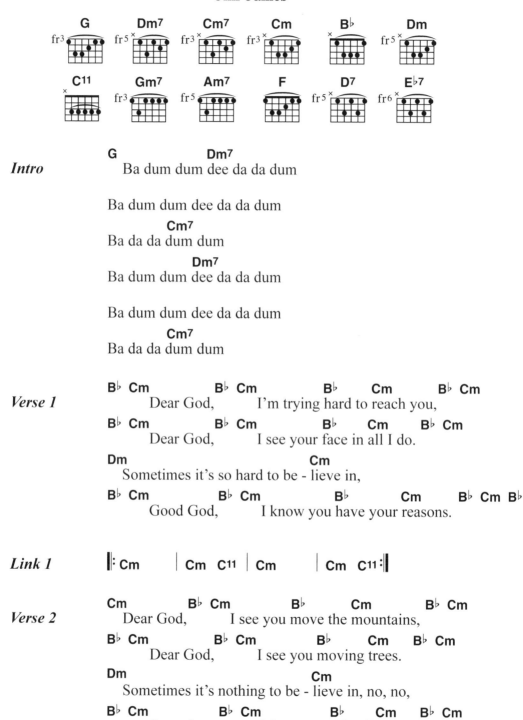

Intro

G   Dm⁷
Ba dum dum dee da da dum

Ba dum dum dee da da dum

Cm⁷
Ba da da dum dum

Dm⁷
Ba dum dum dee da da dum

Ba dum dum dee da da dum

Cm⁷
Ba da da dum dum

Verse 1

B♭ Cm   B♭ Cm   B♭   Cm   B♭ Cm
    Dear God,   I'm trying hard to reach you,
B♭ Cm   B♭ Cm   B♭   Cm   B♭ Cm
    Dear God,   I see your face in all I do.
Dm   Cm
    Sometimes it's so hard to be - lieve in,
B♭ Cm   B♭ Cm   B♭   Cm   B♭ Cm B♭
    Good God,   I know you have your reasons.

Link 1

‖: Cm | Cm   C¹¹ | Cm | Cm   C¹¹ :‖

Verse 2

Cm   B♭ Cm   B♭   Cm   B♭ Cm
    Dear God,   I see you move the mountains,
B♭ Cm   B♭ Cm   B♭   Cm   B♭ Cm
      Dear God,   I see you moving trees.
Dm   Cm
    Sometimes it's nothing to be - lieve in, no, no,
B♭ Cm   B♭ Cm   B♭   Cm   B♭ Cm
    Sometimes   it's every - thing I see.

Chorus 1	**Cm** **Dm⁷** Well I've been thinking about,

Cm⁷

And I've been breaking it down without an answer.

Dm⁷

I know I'm thinking aloud,

                                 Cm⁷

But if your love's still around, why do we suffer?

Why do we suffer?

Link 2 | Gm⁷ | Gm⁷ | Gm⁷ | Gm⁷   ‖

Verse 3

Gm⁷

Dear God, I wish that I could touch you,

How strange sometimes I feel I almost do.

Am⁷   **Gm⁷**

  And then I'm back behind the glass a - gain,

Oh God, what keeps you out, it keeps me in.

Chorus 2

Cm   **Dm⁷**

Well I've been thinking about,

                                 Cm⁷

And I've been breaking it down without an answer.

Dm⁷

I know I'm thinking aloud,

                                 Cm⁷

But if your love's still around, why do we suffer?

Why do we suffer?

Outro

‖: Dm⁷ | Dm⁷ | Cm⁷ | Cm⁷   :‖

| Gm⁷ | Gm⁷ | F | F |

| Dm⁷ | D⁷ | E♭⁷ | F |

| Gm⁷ | Gm⁷ | Gm⁷ | Gm⁷   ‖

Do You Realize??

Words & Music by
Wayne Coyne, Steven Drozd, Michael Ivins & David Fridmann

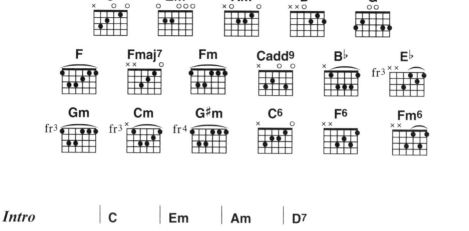

Intro | C | Em | Am | D7

Verse 1

            C   Em   Am   G   F
Do you realize   that you have the most beautiful face?

Fm   C   Em Am   D7
Do you realize   we're floating in space?

          Fmaj7 Em   Am   G
Do you realize   that happiness makes you cry?

F G C   Em   Am   F
Do you realize   that everyone you know

        Fm   C Cadd9 C Cadd9
Some - day will die?

          F   Am   G
And in - stead of saying all of your good - byes, let them know...

Bridge 1

       C   F
You realize that life goes fast,

       C   G
It's hard to make the good things last.

       C   Em
You realize the sun doesn't go down,

       G   F   G   C   Fm
It's just an illusion caused by the world spinning round.

Verse 2

B♭   E♭   Gm Cm G♯m
Do you realize? Oh, oh, oh._____

G   C   Em   Am   F
Do you realize   that everyone you know

         Fm   C   Cadd9
Some - day will die,

         F   Am   G
And in - stead of saying all of your good - byes, let them know...

Bridge 2

       C6
You realize that life goes fast,

   F6
It's hard to make the good things last.

       C6
You realize the sun doesn't go down,

   F6   Fm   Fm6 Fm   Am   G
It's just an illusion caused by the world   spinning round.

Outro

F G C   Em   Am   G   F
Do you realize   that you have the most beautiful face?

Fm   C
Do you realize?

Dream Catch Me

Words & Music by
Crispin Hunt, Newton Faulkner & Gordon Mills

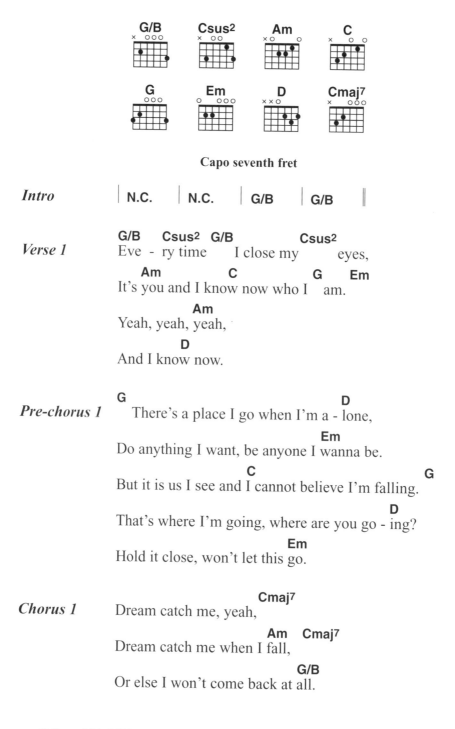

Capo seventh fret

Intro | N.C. | N.C. | G/B | G/B ‖

Verse 1

G/B   Csus2 G/B   Csus2
Eve - ry time   I close my   eyes,
          Am   C   G   Em
It's you and I know now who I   am.
              Am
Yeah, yeah, yeah,
              D
And I know now.

Pre-chorus 1

G   D
   There's a place I go when I'm a - lone,
                                              Em
Do anything I want, be anyone I wanna be.
                        C   G
But it is us I see and I cannot believe I'm falling.
                                                              D
That's where I'm going, where are you go - ing?
                              Em
Hold it close, won't let this go.

Chorus 1

                              Cmaj7
Dream catch me, yeah,
                        Am   Cmaj7
Dream catch me when I fall,
                              G/B
Or else I won't come back at all.

Verse 2

      Csus²   **G/B**   **Csus²**
You do so much   that you don't   know,

    Am   **C**   **Em**   **G**
It's true and I know now who I   am.

         Am
Yeah, yeah, yeah,

     D
And I know now.

Pre-chorus 2   As Pre-chorus 1

     Em   **Cmaj⁷**

Chorus 2   Dream catch me, yeah,

                    Am   **Cmaj⁷**
Dream catch me when I fall,

                     Em
Or else I won't come back at all.

               C   **G**
Bridge   See you as a mountain, a fountain, a god.

              D   **Em**
See you as a descant soul in the setting sun.

          C   **G**
You as a sound as silent as none.

  D
I'm yours.

       G   **D**
Pre-chorus 3   There's a place I go when I'm a - lone,

                            Em
Do anything I want, be anyone I wanna be.

                 C
But it is us I see and I cannot believe I'm falling.

Pre-chorus 4   As Pre-chorus 1

     Em   **Cmaj⁷**
Chorus 3   Dream catch me, yeah,

                    Am   **Cmaj⁷**
Dream catch me when I fall,

                    G
Or else I won't come back at all.

Devil's Spoke

Words & Music by
Laura Marling

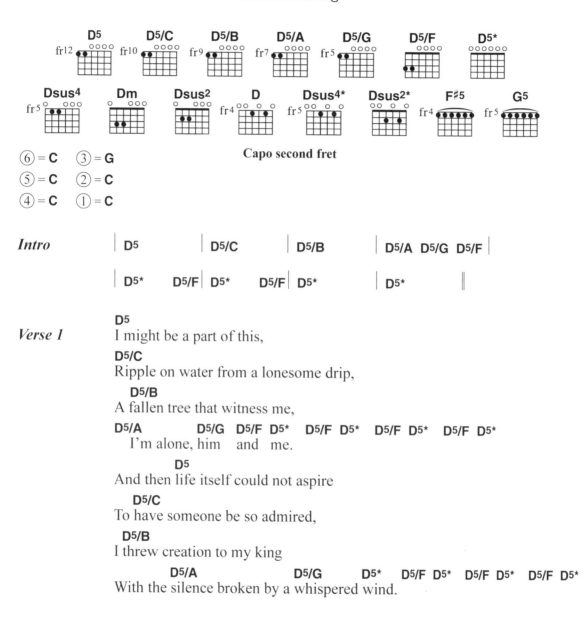

Capo second fret

⑥ = C ③ = G
⑤ = C ② = C
④ = C ① = C

Intro | D5 | D5/C | D5/B | D5/A D5/G D5/F |

| D5*   D5/F| D5*   D5/F| D5* | D5*   ‖

Verse 1
D5
I might be a part of this,
D5/C
Ripple on water from a lonesome drip,
  D5/B
A fallen tree that witness me,
D5/A   **D5/G D5/F D5*** **D5/F D5*** **D5/F D5*** **D5/F D5***
 I'm alone, him   and me.
      D5
And then life itself could not aspire
    D5/C
To have someone be so admired,
   D5/B
I threw creation to my king
       D5/A   **D5/G**   **D5*** **D5/F D5*** **D5/F D5*** **D5/F D5***
With the silence broken by a whispered wind.

Chorus 1

Dsus⁴   Dm Dsus² D⁵*
All of this can be   broken,

Dsus⁴   Dm Dsus² D⁵*
All of this can be   broken,

Dsus⁴   Dm D⁵*
Hold your devil by   his spoke

     Dsus⁴   Dm   D⁵*   D⁵/F D⁵*   D⁵/F D⁵*   D⁵/F D⁵*
And spin him to the ground.

Verse 2

          D⁵
And root to root and tip to tip,

     D⁵/C
I look at him my country gyp.

D⁵/B
Let it up I owe his fears,

          D⁵/A   **D⁵/G D⁵/F D⁵*   D⁵/F D⁵*   D⁵/F D⁵*   D⁵/F D⁵***
But someone brought you close to   tears.

D⁵
Many trains and many miles

          D⁵/C
Brought you to me on this sunny isle,

          D⁵/B
And what of which you wish to speak,

          D⁵/A   **D⁵/G D⁵/F D⁵*   D⁵/F D⁵*   D⁵/F D⁵*   D⁵/F D⁵***
Have you come here to res - cue   me?

Chorus 2

Dsus⁴   Dm Dsus² D⁵*
All of this can be   broken,

Dsus⁴   Dm Dsus² D⁵*
All of this can be   broken,

Dsus⁴   Dm D⁵*
Hold your devil by   his spoke

     Dsus⁴   Dm   D⁵*   D⁵/F D⁵*   D⁵/F D⁵*   D⁵/F D⁵*
And spin him to the ground.

Link 1   ‖: **D** | **Dsus⁴*** | **D** | **Dsus²***   :‖

Bridge

Dsus2 Dsus4* D Dsus2* D5* Dsus4* D   Dsus2* D5* Dsus4*
But the love   of your   life lives   but lies   no more

D   Dsus2* D5* Dsus4* D Dsus2* D5*   D5/F D5*   D5/F D5*   D5/F D5*
And where she lay   a flower grows.

Dsus4* D   Dsus2* D5*   Dsus4* D   Dsus2*
And the arms   have fed   and the babes have wed

D5*   Dsus4* D   Dsus2* D5*
And the backs   have bled,

Dsus4* D Dsus2* D5*   D5/F D5*   D5/F D5*   D5/F D5*
Keep - ing her in tow.

F♯5   G5   D5*
   But I am your keep - er,

F♯5   G5   D5*
   And I hold your face away from light.

F♯5   G5   D5*
   I am yours till they come,

F♯5   G5   D5*
   I am yours till they come.

Verse 3

D5   D5/C
   Eye to eye,   nose to nose,

D5/B   D5/A
   Ripping off each other's clothes

                    D5/G D5/F D5*   D5/F D5*   D5/F D5*   D5/F D5*
In a most pe - cu - liar way.

D5   D5/C
   Eye to eye,   nose to nose,

D5/B   D5/A
   Ripping off each other's clothes

                    D5/G D5/F D5*   D5/F D5*   D5/F D5*   D5/F D5*
In a most pe - cu - liar way.

Outro

D5   D5/C   D5/B   D5/A   D5/G D5/F D5*
Mmm, mmm, mmm, mmm.

44

Ryan Adams

Everybody Knows

Words & Music by
Ryan Adams, Neal Casal, Brad Pemberton & Jon Graboff

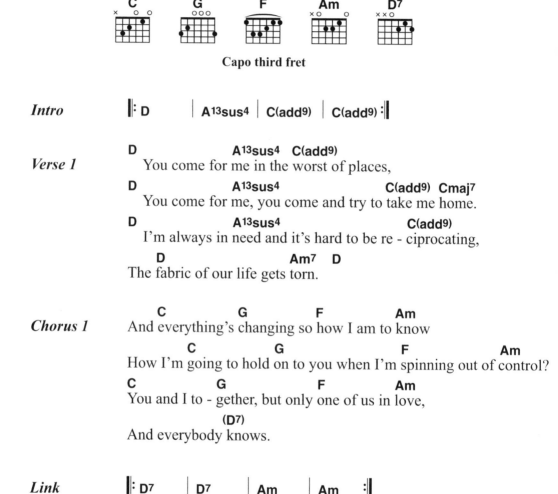

Capo third fret

Intro

‖: D | A¹³sus⁴ | C(add⁹) | C(add⁹) :‖

Verse 1

D   A¹³sus⁴   C(add⁹)
You come for me in the worst of places,

D   A¹³sus⁴   C(add⁹)   Cmaj⁷
You come for me, you come and try to take me home.

D   A¹³sus⁴   C(add⁹)
I'm always in need and it's hard to be re - ciprocating,

D   Am⁷   D
The fabric of our life gets torn.

Chorus 1

C   G   F   Am
And everything's changing so how I am to know

C   G   F   Am
How I'm going to hold on to you when I'm spinning out of control?

C   G   F   Am
You and I to - gether, but only one of us in love,

             (D⁷)
And everybody knows.

Link

‖: D⁷ | D⁷ | Am | Am :‖

Verse 2

D   A^{13}sus^4 C(add^9)
He says her name, it echoes in my head like it was a canyon,

D   A^{13}sus^4 C(add^9)   Cmaj^7
He says her name, he says it and I know what's up.

D   A^{13}sus^4 C(add^9)
You come to me sometimes when I'm thinking like a

Cannonball shooting out a cannon,

D   Am^7 D
And I forget whatever it was I was thinking about.

Chorus 2

        C   G   F   Am
With everything changing how am I to know

           C   G   F   Am
How I'm going to hold on to you when I'm spinning out of control?

C   G   F   Am
You and I to - gether, but only one of us in love,

              (D^7)
And everybody knows.

Outro

| D^7 | D^7 | Am | Am | |

| D^7 | D^7 | Am | ‖

Am   D^7 Am D^7 Am
Everybody knows.

Elusive

Words & Music by
Scott Matthews

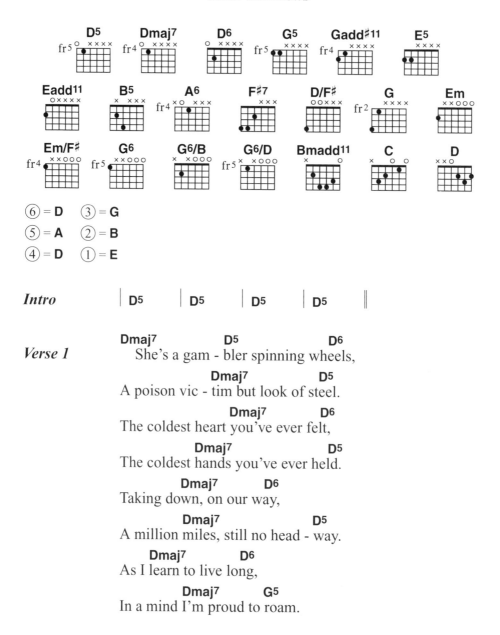

⑥ = D ③ = G
⑤ = A ② = B
④ = D ① = E

Intro | D5 | D5 | D5 | D5   ‖

Verse 1

       Dmaj7   D5   D6
She's a gam - bler spinning wheels,

       Dmaj7   D5
A poison vic - tim but look of steel.

       Dmaj7   D6
The coldest heart you've ever felt,

       Dmaj7   D5
The coldest hands you've ever held.

       Dmaj7   D6
Taking down, on our way,

       Dmaj7   D5
A million miles, still no head - way.

       Dmaj7   D6
As I learn to live long,

       Dmaj7   G5
In a mind I'm proud to roam.

Chorus 1

G5   Gadd♯11   E5
She's elu - sive and I'm a - wake,

                Eadd11   B5
You're finally real, there's nothing fake.

                          A6
A mystery now to me and you,

                              F♯7
Open my eyes and I'm next to you.

    D/F♯   G Gadd♯11   G   D5
She said my desti - ny lies in the hands that set me free.

Verse 2

Dmaj7   D5   D6
  A reckless night, she hears me breathe,

                Dmaj7   D5
Cursing the sky at this compa - ny.

                  Dmaj7   D6
They lost the wis - dom deep in - side,

                Dmaj7   D5
When bitter - ness shows its side.

          Dmaj7   D6
If it's true, I am doom - ed,

                Dmaj7   D5
What more is there to hold on to?

                Dmaj7   D6
A strand of her hair is all I own,

          Dmaj7   G5
A gift to me, this sorry soul.

Chorus 2

G5   Gadd♯11   E5
She's elu - sive and I'm a - wake,

                Eadd11   B5
You're finally real, there's nothing fake.

                          A6
A mystery now to me and you,

                            F♯7
Open my eyes and I'm next to you.

    D/F♯   G   Gadd♯11 G   (Em)
She said my desti - ny lies in the   hands that set me free.

Link 1

‖: Em Em/F♯ G6 G6/B G6/D :‖ *Play 3 times*

| Em Em/F♯ G6 | D5 | D5 | ‖

Verse 3

Dmaj7   D5   D6
The sun in sails, and this ain't right.

      Dmaj7   D5
There's more to her than meets the eye.

     Dmaj7   D6
She comes and goes at any time,

     Dmaj7   G5
Back in my head another time.

Chorus 3

G5   Em
She's elusive and I'm a - wake,

            B5
You're finally real, there's nothing fake.

        A6
A mystery now to me and you,

          F♯7
Open my eyes and I'm next to you.

        G   Bmadd11
She said my destiny lies in the hands that set me free.

Outro

Bmadd11 C D
Ooh,   ooh, ooh, ooh, ooh, ooh, ooh, ooh, ooh.___

Bmadd11 C D
Ooh,   ooh, ooh, ooh, ooh, ooh, ooh, ooh, ooh.___

Bmadd11 C D
Ooh,   ooh, ooh, ooh, ooh, ooh, ooh, ooh, ooh.___

Bmadd11 C
Ooh,   ooh.

‖: D5 | D5 | D5 | D5 :‖

Eyes Are At The Billions

Words & Music by
Cortney Tidwell

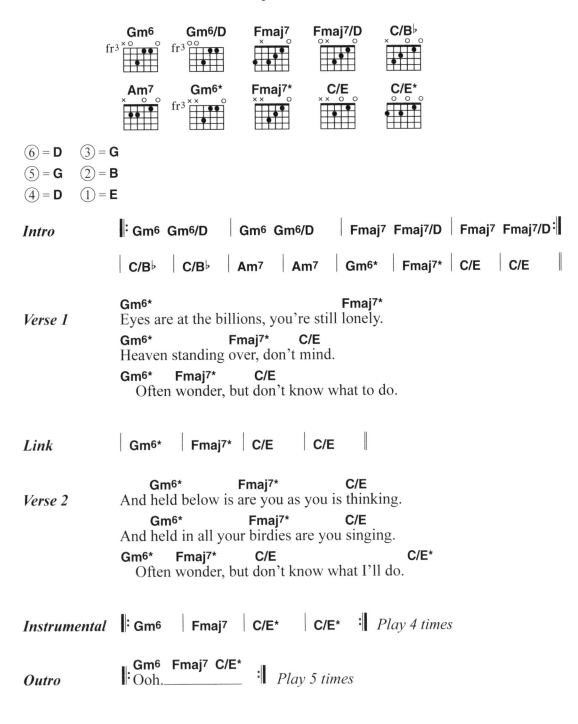

⑥ = D   ③ = G
⑤ = G   ② = B
④ = D   ① = E

Intro   ‖: Gm⁶ Gm⁶/D │ Gm⁶ Gm⁶/D │ Fmaj⁷ Fmaj⁷/D │ Fmaj⁷ Fmaj⁷/D :‖

│ C/B♭ │ C/B♭ │ Am⁷ │ Am⁷ │ Gm⁶* │ Fmaj⁷* │ C/E │ C/E ‖

Verse 1

Gm⁶*   Fmaj⁷*
Eyes are at the billions, you're still lonely.

Gm⁶*   Fmaj⁷*   C/E
Heaven standing over, don't mind.

Gm⁶*   Fmaj⁷*   C/E
  Often wonder, but don't know what to do.

Link   │ Gm⁶* │ Fmaj⁷* │ C/E │ C/E ‖

Verse 2

         Gm⁶*   Fmaj⁷*   C/E
And held below is are you as you is thinking.

         Gm⁶*   Fmaj⁷*   C/E
And held in all your birdies are you singing.

Gm⁶*   Fmaj⁷*   C/E   C/E*
  Often wonder, but don't know what I'll do.

Instrumental   ‖: Gm⁶ │ Fmaj⁷ │ C/E* │ C/E* :‖ *Play 4 times*

Outro   ‖: Gm⁶ Fmaj⁷ C/E*
Ooh._____ :‖ *Play 5 times*

Everyday

Words & Music by
Andy Cabic

F#   A#m   C#m   B   C#9

F#7   Bm   G#m   C#   D#m   G#

Intro

‖: F# | A#m | F# | A#m :‖

Verse 1

F#   A#m C#m   B   F#   A#m   B C#9
Every day,   I'm a - way from you shakes me   up in - side.

F#   F#7   B   Bm
I wanna be near you,   know that you are here

G#m A#m   B
Lying just next to me,

     G#m   B   (F#)
How happy we'd both be.

Link

| F# | A#m | F# | A#m ‖

Verse 2

F#   A#m C#m   B   F#
I say it all the time,   you don't pay no mind when I tell you

     A#m   B   C#9
That I love you, now do you?

F#   F#7 B   Bm   G#m
I wanna be clear,   all I wanna hear is your voice,

     A#m   B
Have your face to see

     G#m   B   (F#)
How happy that would make me.

Interlude

F♯ A♯m B   C♯   D♯m
      Do do do do do

F♯   A♯m B C♯   D♯m
  Do____ do do do do do

C♯
Do do do do do do do

B C♯
    Do do do do do do do

B C♯   B   A♯m C♯ F♯ A♯m B C♯9
    Do do do do do do do

Bridge

F♯   A♯m   B   C♯9
  I alway seem to make something out of noth - ing,

    F♯   A♯m   B C♯ D♯m
But I   can't make you ap - pear.

      G♯   B   C♯   F♯
While I'm a - way, just know I'll play this song for you and wait.

A♯m B C♯9   F♯
    Wait for me now.

A♯m B C♯9   F♯
    Wait for me now.

A♯m B C♯9   F♯
  Oh, wait for me now.

‖: A♯m B C♯9   F♯
      Oh, oh, oh, oh

Outro

A♯m B C♯9   F♯
Wait for me now. :‖ *Repeat to fade*

Factory

Words & Music by
Benjamin Bridwell

C   Am   Em   G   Bm   D

Intro

‖: C | Am | Em | G :‖

Verse 1

(G)   C   Am   Em   G
The ele - vator in the hotel lobby has a lazy door,

     C   Am   Em   G
The man inside is going to a hotel room.

     C   Am   Em   G
He jumped out right after seeing just the very sight of me,

       C   Am   Em G
De - cided he better hike it to the second floor.

Bridge 1

Bm   Em Bm   Em
   It's tempo - rary,   this place I'm in,

Bm   Em   Bm   Em
   I perma - nently won't do   this a - gain,

         C   D
My be - longings scattered all across the hotel floor.

Link 1

‖: C | Am | Em | G :‖

Verse 2

(G)   C   Am   Em   G
Now and later, I was thinking it over by the snack machine,

C   Am   Em G
  I thought a - bout you and a candy bar.

           C   Am   Em   G
And now and later, now that I've got it stuck be - tween my teeth,

C   Am   Em G
I fell asleep to the greatest movie of the year.

Bridge 2

|Bm|Em|Bm|Em|
A man gets lonely   for heaven's sake,

|Bm|Em|Bm|Em|
He's wondering on - ly what did you do to - day,

|C|D|
The world is spinning around into an old sad song.

Link 2   ‖: C | Am | Em | G   :‖

Verse 3

(G) C   Am   Em   G
Well it's coming down out - side like I've never even seen before,

C   Am   Em G
I fell into some kind of sorry state.

C   Am   Em   G
But looking back now, I think it's finally time for me to laugh about it

C   Am   Em
And get my things together and find something to say.

Bridge 3

|Bm|Em|Bm|Em|
Well, I feel awful   and I be - lieve

|Bm|Em|Bm|Em|
That time gets wasted in this   mise - ry,

|C|D|
And darling I don't ever wanna come back home.

Outro   ‖: C | Am | Em | G   :‖ *Play 4 times*

          | C   ‖

Fake Empire

Words & Music by
Matt Berninger & Bryce Dessner

C   C/F   C/G   C/A   G   F   Am

Intro   ‖: C | C/F | C/G | C/G :‖

Verse 1
C   C/F   C/G
Stay out super late   tonight picking apples, making pies,
C   C/F   C/G
Put a little something in our lemon - ade and take it with us.
                  C/A   C/F   G
We're half - awake in a fake empire.
                  C/A   C/F   G
We're half - awake in a fake empire.

Verse 2
C   C/F   C/G
Tiptoe through our shiny city with our diamond slippers on,
C   C/F   C/G
Do our gay ballet   on ice, bluebirds on our shoulders.
                  C/A   C/F   G
We're half - awake in a fake empire.
                  C/A   C/F   G
We're half - awake in a fake empire.

Instrumental   ‖: F | Am | G | G :‖

                       ‖: Am | G | Am | G :‖

Verse 3

    C   C/F   C/G
Turn the light out say goodnight, no   thinking for a little while,

    C   C/F   C/G
Let's not try to figure out everything at once.

        C   C/F   C/G
It's hard to keep track of you falling through the sky.

           C/A   C/F   G
We're half - awake in a fake empire.

           C/A   C/F   G
We're half - awake in a fake empire.

Outro

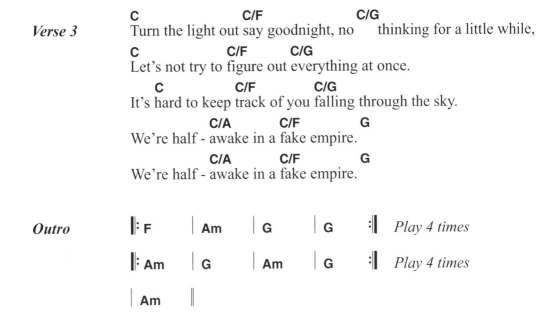

‖: F | Am | G | G :‖   *Play 4 times*

‖: Am | G | Am | G :‖   *Play 4 times*

| Am ‖

Fans

Words & Music by
Caleb Followill, Nathan Followill, Jared Followill & Matthew Followill

E   Aadd9/E   Badd11/E

Intro

‖ E | E |

‖: E   Aadd9/E | Badd11/E   Aadd9/E |

| E   Aadd9/E | Badd11/E   Aadd9/E :‖

2° (Home-)

Verse 1

E
Home - grown.

Aadd9/E   Badd11/E Aadd9/E   E
Rock to the rhythm and bop to the beat of the ra - dio.

Aadd9/E   Badd11/E   Aadd9/E E
You ain't got the slang but you got the face to   play the role.

Aadd9/E   Badd11/E Aadd9/E   E   Aadd9/E Badd11/E
And you can play with me._____

Verse 2

E
And all the bro's,

Aadd9/E   Badd11/E Aadd9/E   E
Try for the courage and try for   charity's tight clothes.

Aadd9/E   Badd11/E Aadd9/E   E
She's got a hat and all the   hat says is asshole,

Aadd9/E   Badd11/E   Aadd9/E   E   Aadd9/E Badd11/E
She'll be bobbing to me._____

Chorus 1

Aadd9/E   E
Pretty hairdos,

Aadd9/E   Badd11/E   Aadd9/E E
And those lipstick kisses blown yeah that's the right move.

Aadd9/E   Badd11/E   Aadd9/E E
Make me feel like I'm the one who   moves you,

Aadd9/E   Badd11/E   Aadd9/E   E   Aadd9/E Badd11/E
The only one you see. _____

Verse 3
E
Now take it down.

Aadd9/E   Badd11/E   Aadd9/E E
Don't you let those tears quench the   thirs - ty ground.

Aadd9/E   Badd11/E Aadd9/E   E
Don't you be so scared that you   can't make a sound.

Aadd9/E   Badd11/E Aadd9/E E Aadd9/E Badd11/E
Make a sound for me. _____

Aadd9/E   E
Chorus 2   All of London sing,

        Aadd9/E   Badd11/E   Aadd9/E E
'Cause England swings and they sure love the tales I bring.

             Aadd9/E   Badd11/E   Aadd9/E E
And those rainy days they ain't so bad when you're   the king,

        Aadd9/E   Badd11/E Aadd9/E E
The king they want to see. _____

| Aadd9/E   Badd11/E Aadd9/E ‖

Guitar Solo ‖: E   Aadd9/E | Badd11/E Aadd9/E |

         | E   Aadd9/E | Badd11/E Aadd9/E :‖
                                               2º (Home-)

Verse 4   As Verse 1

Aadd9/E   E
Chorus 3 Pretty hair - dos,

             Aadd9/E   Badd11/E   Aadd9/E   E
And those lipstick kisses blown yeah that's the right move.

Aadd9/E   Badd11/E   Aadd9/E   E
Make me feel like I'm the one who's mov - in' you,

        Aadd9/E   Badd11/E Aadd9/E E Aadd9/E Badd11/E
The only one you see. _____

Chorus 4   As Chorus 2

Outro   ‖: E   Aadd9/E | Badd11/E Aadd9/E |

         | E   Aadd9/E | Badd11/E Aadd9/E :‖ E   ‖

Flightless Bird, American Mouth

Words & Music by
Samuel Beam

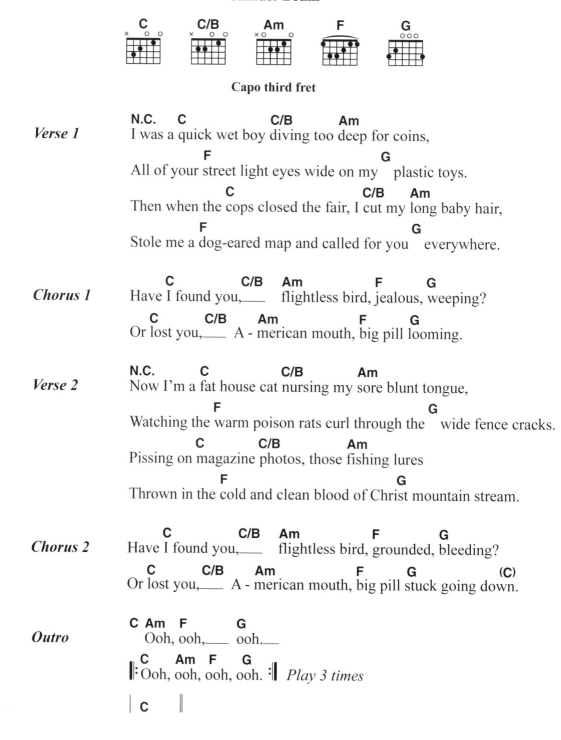

Capo third fret

Verse 1

N.C.   C   C/B   Am
I was a quick wet boy diving too deep for coins,

          F   G
All of your street light eyes wide on my   plastic toys.

                    C   C/B   Am
Then when the cops closed the fair, I cut my long baby hair,

          F   G
Stole me a dog-eared map and called for you   everywhere.

Chorus 1

        C   C/B   Am   F   G
Have I found you,___ flightless bird, jealous, weeping?

     C   C/B   Am   F   G
Or lost you,___ A - merican mouth, big pill looming.

Verse 2

N.C.   C   C/B   Am
Now I'm a fat house cat nursing my sore blunt tongue,

            F   G
Watching the warm poison rats curl through the   wide fence cracks.

              C   C/B   Am
Pissing on magazine photos, those fishing lures

          F   G
Thrown in the cold and clean blood of Christ mountain stream.

Chorus 2

        C   C/B   Am   F   G
Have I found you,___ flightless bird, grounded, bleeding?

     C   C/B   Am   F   G   (C)
Or lost you,___ A - merican mouth, big pill stuck going down.

Outro

C Am F   G
  Ooh, ooh,___ ooh.___

     C   Am F   G
‖: Ooh, ooh, ooh, ooh. :‖ *Play 3 times*

  | C   ‖

For Emma

Words & Music by
Justin Vernon

C   Em/G   Am⁷/F   Fmaj⁷

Tune guitar slightly flat

Intro ‖: C | C | Em/G | Em/G | Am⁷/F | Am⁷/F | C | C :‖

Verse 1

Em/G C
    So apropos,

Em/G   C
    Saw death on a sunny snow.

          Fmaj⁷   C
For every life, forego the parable,

          Fmaj⁷   C
Seek the light, my knees are cold.

Em/G   Am⁷/F   C
    Running home, running home, running home, run - ning home.

Verse 2

Em/G C   C
    Go find an - other lover

Em/G   C
    To bring a, to string a - long.

          Fmaj⁷   C
With all your lies, you're still very loveable.

Em/G   Fmaj⁷   C
    I toured the light, so many foreign roads.

Em/G   Am⁷/F
    For Emma, for - ever ago.

Instrumental

| C | C | Em/G | Em/G | Am⁷/F | Am⁷/F | C | C | |

| C | C | Em/G | Em/G | Am⁷/F | Am⁷/F | C | |

| Em/G | Em/G | C | C ‖

Outro

Fmaj⁷   C   Fmaj⁷   C Em/G Am⁷/F C
      Mm.__   Mm._____

| C | C | Em/G | Em/G |

| Am⁷/F | Am⁷/F | C | Em/G | Em/G ‖

Fight Test

Words & Music by
Wayne Coyne, Steven Drozd, Michael Ivans, David Fridmann & Cat Stevens

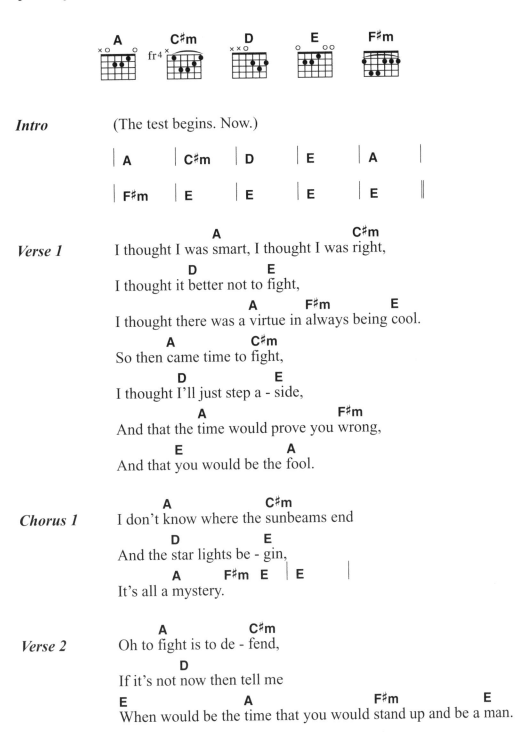

Intro

(The test begins. Now.)

| A | C♯m | D | E | A |
| F♯m | E | E | E | E |

Verse 1

               A   C♯m
I thought I was smart, I thought I was right,

        D   E
I thought it better not to fight,

                 A   F♯m   E
I thought there was a virtue in always being cool.

        A   C♯m
So then came time to fight,

      D   E
I thought I'll just step a - side,

            A   F♯m
And that the time would prove you wrong,

      E   A
And that you would be the fool.

Chorus 1

        A   C♯m
I don't know where the sunbeams end

      D   E
And the star lights be - gin,

      A   F♯m E | E |
It's all a mystery.

Verse 2

        A   C♯m
Oh to fight is to de - fend,

        D
If it's not now then tell me

E   A   F♯m   E
When would be the time that you would stand up and be a man.

cont.

        A   **F♯m**
For to lose I could ac - cept,

             D   **E**
But to sur - render I just wept

                 A   **F♯m**
And regretted this moment

          E
Oh that I,

Chorus 2

         A   **C♯m**
I don't know where the sunbeams end

         D   **E**
And the star lights be - gin,

         A   **F♯m** **E**
It's all a mystery.

            A   **C♯m**
And I don't know how a man decides

         D   **E**
What's right for his own life,

         A   **F♯m E** | **E** |
It's all a mystery.

Verse 3

          A   **C♯m**
'Cause I'm a man, not a boy,

            D   **E**
And there are things you can't a - void,

        A
You have to face them,

         F♯m   **E**
When you're not prepared to face them.

   A   **C♯m**
If I could I would,

           D
But you're with him now,

    E
It do no good,

         A
I should have fought him

      F♯m   **E**
But in - stead I let him,

       A
I let him take you.

64

Chorus 3

<pre>
      A   C#m
I don't know where the sunbeams end
         D   E
And the star lights be - gin,
        A   F#m E
It's all a mystery.
            A   C#m
And I don't know how a man decides
         D   E
What's right for his own life,
           A   F#m E
It's all a mystery.
</pre>

Bridge

<pre>
| D | D | E | E | D |
| D | E | E | E | E   ‖
</pre>

Chorus 4

<pre>
      A   C#m
I don't know where the sunbeams end
         D   E
And the star lights be - gin,
        A
It's all a mystery.
            F#m   E
(Won't you stand up and be a man)
            A   C#m
And I don't know how a man decides
         D   E
What's right for his own life,
        A
It's all a mystery.
             F#m   E
(When you're not prepared to face them.)
      A   C#m
I don't know where the sunbeams end
         D   E
And the star lights be - gin,
        A
It's all a mystery.
            F#m   E | E |
(But in - stead I let him take you)
                   A
It's all a myste - ry.
     N.C.
(The test is over. Now.)
</pre>

First Day Of My Life

Words & Music by
Conor Oberst

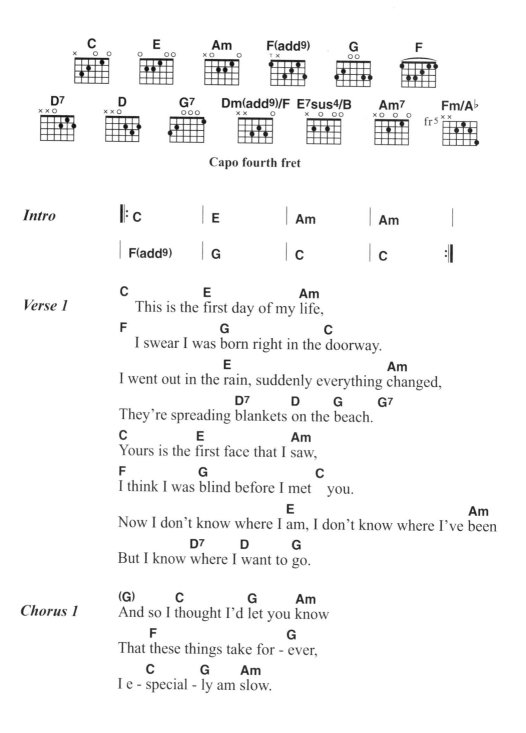

Capo fourth fret

Intro

‖: C | E | Am | Am |
| F(add9) | G | C | C :‖

Verse 1

```
    C              E            Am
     This is the first day of my life,
    F              G              C
     I swear I was born right in the doorway.
                    E                      Am
     I went out in the rain, suddenly everything changed,
                      D7      D     G    G7
     They're spreading blankets on the beach.
    C              E            Am
     Yours is the first face that I saw,
    F          G              C
     I think I was blind before I met   you.
                          E                         Am
     Now I don't know where I am, I don't know where I've been
                      D7      D     G
     But I know where I want to go.
```

Chorus 1

```
    (G)      C        G     Am
     And so I thought I'd let you know
          F                      G
     That these things take for - ever,
          C       G    Am
     I e - special - ly am slow.
```

cont.

Dm(add9)/F
But I realise that I need you

                                       C
And I wondered if I could come home.

    E7sus4/B   Am Dm(add9)/F Fm/A♭
Mm,_____ mm.____

Verse 2

 C   E   Am
  Remember the time you drove all night

 F   G   C
  Just to meet me in the morning.

 C   E   Am
  And I thought it was strange you said everything changed,

           D7   D   G G7
You felt as if you'd just woke up.

            C   E   Am
And you said "This is the first day of my life,

 F   G   C
  I'm glad I didn't die before I met   you.

                E   Am
But now I don't care I could go any - where with you

        D7   D   G
And I'd probably be hap - py."

Chorus 2

(G)   C   G   Am
So if you want to be with me,

        F   G
With these things there's no telling,

       C   G   Am
We just have to wait and see.

                Dm(add9)/F
But I'd rather be working for a paycheck

                            C
Than waiting to win the lottery.

    E7sus4/B Am
Uh huh, mm, mm.

               Dm(add9)/F
Besides may - be this time is different,

                                C   E7sus4/B Am7
I mean I really think you like me,__ ee,_____ ee.

Dm(add9)/F   Fm/A♭
       Ee._____

Outro

C	E7sus4/B	Am7	Am7	
Dm(add9)/F	Dm(add9)/F	Fm/A♭	Fm/A♭	C

67

Flume

Words & Music by
Justin Vernon

C   Em   Am   G   Gsus4   F   E   Fmaj7

Tune guitar slightly flat

Intro

| C | C | Em | Em |

| Am | Am | Em | Em |

Verse 1

C   Em   G   Gsus4 G Gsus4 G Gsus4 G
I am my mother's only one, it's e - nough.

C   Em   G   Gsus4 G
I wear my garment so it shows, now you know.

Chorus 1

F   Am   C
Only love is all ma - roon,

F   Am   G
Gluey feathers on a flume,

F   Am
Sky is womb, she's the moon.

Link 1

| C | C | Em | Em |

| Am | Am | Em | Em |

Verse 2

C   Em   G   Gsus4 G Gsus4 G Gsus4 G
I am my mother on the wall with us all.

C   Em   G   Gsus4 G
I move in water, shore to shore, nothing's more.

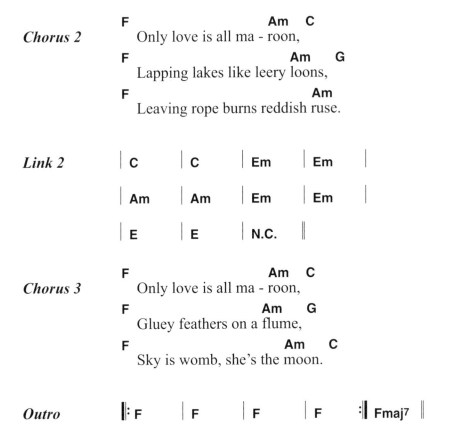

Chorus 2

F   Am   C

Only love is all ma - roon,

F   Am   G

Lapping lakes like leery loons,

F   Am

Leaving rope burns reddish ruse.

Link 2

| C | C | Em | Em | |

| Am | Am | Em | Em | |

| E | E | N.C. ‖

Chorus 3

F   Am   C

Only love is all ma - roon,

F   Am   G

Gluey feathers on a flume,

F   Am   C

Sky is womb, she's the moon.

Outro

‖: F | F | F | F   :‖ Fmaj⁷ ‖

Forget Her

Words & Music by
Jeff Buckley

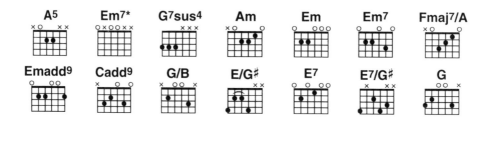

Intro   ‖: A5 | Em7* G7sus4 | A5 | Em7* G7sus4 :‖

Verse 1

Am
   Now this town is busy sleeping,
Em
   All the noise has died away.
Am
   I walk the streets to stop my weeping,
                        Em7
'Cause she'll never change her ways.

Chorus 1

         Fmaj7/A
But don't fool yourself,

                               Emadd9
She was heartache from the moment that you met her.
        Fmaj7/A
Ah, my heart feels so still,
                  Cadd9
As I try to find the will to forget her somehow,
G/B Em7   (A5)
Oh, I think I've forgotten her now.

Link | A5 | Em7* G7sus4 | A5 | Em7* G7sus4 |
   (now.)

Verse 2

Am
Her love is a rose pale and dying,

Em⁷
  Dropping her petals in pain I know.

Am
  All full of wine the world before her

    Em⁷
Was sober with no place to go.

Chorus 2

    Fmaj⁷/A
Don't fool yourself,

                      Emadd⁹
She was heartache from the moment that you met her.

    Fmaj⁷/A
My heart is frozen still

            Cadd⁹
As I try to find the will to forget her somehow,

G/B   **Em⁷**   **(Am)**
  She's somewhere out there now.

Guitar solo

Am	Am	Am	Am	
(now.)				
Em⁷	Em⁷	Em⁷	Em⁷	
Fmaj⁷/A	Fmaj⁷/A	Fmaj⁷/A	Fmaj⁷/A	
Em⁷	Em⁷	Em⁷	Em⁷	
Am	Am	Am	Am	
Cadd⁹	Cadd⁹	G/B	Em	

                                          (Oh, my)

Verse 3

       A5   **Em7***
Oh, my tears falling down,

       G7sus4 **A5**   **Em7***
As I try to forget, her love was a joke

        G7sus4   **A5**
From the day that we met,

       Em7* **G7sus4** **A5**
All of the words, all of the men,

       Em7*   **G7sus4**   **A5**
All of my pain when I think back to when…

         Em7* **G7sus4**   **A5**
Remember her hair as it shone in the sun,

         Em7*   **G7sus4**   **A5**
The smell of the bed when I knew what she'd done,

           Em7* **G7sus4**
You tell yourself over and over

   E/G♯   **E7**
You won't ever meet her again.

Chorus 3

           Fmaj7/A
But don't fool yourself,

                       Emadd9
She was heartache from the moment that you met her.

      Fmaj7/A
Oh my heart is frozen still,

                Cadd9
As I try to find the will to forget her somehow,

  G/B   **E7/G♯**
She's out there somewhere now.

Chorus 4

Fmaj7/A   **Emadd9**
Oh,_____ she was heartache from the day that I first met her,

  Fmaj7/A
My heart is frozen still,

                 Cadd9
As I try to find the will to forget you somehow,

    G/B   **G**
'Cause I know you're somewhere out there right now.

Outro

‖: **Fmaj7/A** | **Fmaj7/A** | **Fmaj7/A** | **Fmaj7/A** |

| **Em7** | **Em7** | **Em7** | **Em7** :‖

w/vocal ad lib. to fade

Four Winds

Words & Music by
Conor Oberst

F#m   D   A   Bm   E

Capo first fret

Intro

‖: F#m | D | A | Bm |

| A | Bm | D | D :‖ *Play 4 times*

Verse 1

F#m   D
Your class, your caste, your country, sect, your name or your tribe.
           A   Bm
There's people always dying, trying to keep them alive.
           A   Bm
There's bodies decomposing in con - tainers tonight,
           D
In an a - bandoned building where…
       F#m   D
A squatter's made a mural of a Mexican girl,
           A   Bm
With fifteen cans of spray paint in a chemical swirl.
           A   Bm
She's standing in the ashes at the end of the world,
               D
Four winds   blowing through her hair.

Chorus 1

(D)   Bm   E   Bm   E
But when great Satan's gone, the whore of Baby - lon,
           D   A   D   A
She just can't sus - tain the pressure where it's placed.
       Bm   E
She caves.

Link 1

| F♯m | D | A | Bm | |
| A | Bm | D | D | ‖ |

Verse 2

F♯m   D
The Bible's blind, the Torah's deaf, the Qu'ran's mute.
      A   Bm
If you burn them all together you get close to the truth still,
      A   Bm
They're pouring over Sanskrit on the Ivy League moons,
               D
While shadows   lengthen in the sun.
        F♯m   D
Cast on a school of meditation built to soften the times,
    A   Bm
And hold us at the centre while the spiral unwinds.
    A   Bm
It's knocking over fences, crossing property lines,
           D
Four winds,   cry until it comes.

Chorus 2

(D)   Bm   E
And it's the son of man,
                 Bm   E
Slouching towards Bethle - hem.
             D   A   D   A
A heart just can't con - tain all of that empty space.
  Bm   E
It breaks, it breaks, it breaks.

Link 2

| F♯m | D | F♯m | A | |
| F♯m | D | E | E | ‖ |

(Well I went)

Verse 3

    (E)   F♯m   D
Well, I went back by rented Cadillac and company jet,

        A   Bm
Like a newly orphaned refugee, re - tracing my steps.

        A   Bm
All the way to Cassadaga to com - mune with the dead.

             D
They said, "You'd better look alive."

         F♯m   D
And I was off to old Dakota where a genocide sleeps,

        A   Bm
In the black hills, the bad lands, the calloused east.

     A   Bm
I buried my ballast, I made my peace,

              D
With four winds   levelling the pines.

Chorus 3

               Bm   E   Bm   E
But when great Satan's gone, the whore of Baby - lon,

                     D   A   D   A
Well she just can't re - main with all that outer space.

        Bm   E
She breaks, she breaks,

        Bm   E   F♯m
She caves, she caves.

Laura Marling

Ghosts

Words & Music by
Laura Marling

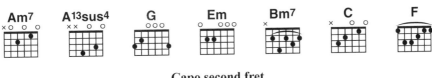

Capo second fret

Intro | Am⁷ | A¹³sus⁴ | A¹³sus⁴ | G | A¹³sus⁴ | G   ‖

Verse 1
A¹³sus⁴   G   A¹³sus⁴
   He walked down a busy street staring solely at his feet,
                                      G
Clutching pictures of past lovers at his side.
A¹³sus⁴   G   A¹³sus⁴
   Stood at the table where she sat and removed his hat
                        G
In respect of her presence.
A¹³sus⁴   G
   Presents her with the pictures and says,
                A¹³sus⁴   G
These are just ghosts that broke my heart before I met you.
                A¹³sus⁴   G
These are just ghosts that broke my heart before I met you.

Verse 2
A¹³sus⁴   G   A¹³sus⁴
   Opened up his little heart, unlocked the lock that kept it dark
                          G   A¹³sus⁴
And read a written warn - ing saying I'm still mourn - ing
               G
Over ghosts, over ghosts, over ghosts,
     A¹³sus⁴   G
Over ghosts that broke my heart before I met you.

Chorus 1

Em   G   Em   G
Lover, please do not   fall to your knees,

       Em   G   Em   G
It's not   like I be - lieve in everlasting love.

Link 1

| A¹³sus⁴ | G | A¹³sus⁴ | G   ‖

$A^{13}sus^{4}$ | G | $A^{13}sus^{4}$ | G ‖

Verse 3

A¹³sus⁴   G   A¹³sus⁴
Said he went crazy at nine - teen, said he lost all his self e - steem

And couldn't understand why he was
G   A¹³sus⁴   G   A¹³sus⁴ G
Cry, cry,_____ cry - ing, cry - ing.
A¹³sus⁴   G
He would stare at empty chairs,

                                    A¹³sus⁴
Think of the ghosts who once sat there,

                     G
The ghosts that broke his heart,

                      A¹³sus⁴
Oh, the ghosts that broke my heart.

                     G
The ghosts that broke his heart,

                      A¹³sus⁴
Oh, the ghosts that broke my heart.

                     G
The ghosts, the ghosts, the ghosts, the ghosts, the ghosts, the ghosts,

      A¹³sus⁴   G
The ghosts that broke my heart before I met you.

Chorus 2   As Chorus 1

Bridge 1

(G)   Am7 Bm7 Am7 Bm7   Am7
He says I'm so   lost, not at all well

Bridge 2

C   Em F C
Ooh._____

        Em F C
Ooh._____

C   Em
    Do as done and there is nothing left to be,

      F   C
Well, it turned out I'd been following him and he'd been following me.

            Em
Do as done, after it was over

F   C
We were just two lovers crying on each other's shoulder and I say.

Chorus 3

Em   G   Em   G
    Lover, please do not   fall to your knees,

      Em   G   Em   G
It's not   like I be - lieve in everlasting love.

Em   G   Em   G
    Lover, please do not   fall to your knees,

      Em   G   Em   G
It's not   like I be - lieve in everlasting love.

Golden

Words & Music by
Jim James

E E6 B7sus2 B7 B6 B6sus4 B11
B9 B7(no3) B6(no3) Emaj7 A B C#m

⑥ = E   ③ = G
⑤ = B   ② = B
④ = E   ① = E

Capo first fret

Intro

| E | E6 | B7sus2 | B7 | B6 |

| B6sus4 | B11 | B9 | B9 | B9 ‖

Verse 1

E
Watching a stretch of road, miles of light explode,
B7(no3)
B6(no3)   B11
Drifting off a thing I've nev - er done before.
E   B7(no3)
Watching a crowd roll in, out go the lights, it begins,
B6(no3)   B11   B9
A feeling in my bones I nev - er felt before,   mmm.

Link 1

‖: Emaj7 | Emaj7 | Emaj7 | Emaj7 |

| B9 | B9 | B9 | B9 :‖

Chorus 1

A   B   E   C#
People always told me that bars are dark and lonely,
        A   B   E
And talk is often cheap and filled with air.
A   B   E   C#m
Sure sometimes they thrill me, but nothing could ever chill me
        A   B   E
Like the way they make the time just disap - pear.

Interlude 1	E		E6		B7sus2	B7		B6		

	B6sus4		B11		B9		B9		B9	‖

Verse 2

E   B7(no3)
Feeling you here again hot on my skin again,
B6(no3)   B11
Feeling good, a thing I've nev - er known before.
E   B7(no3)
What does it mean to feel? Millions of dreams come real.
B6(no3)   B11
A feeling in my soul I've nev - er felt before, mmm.

Link 2

As Link 1

Chorus 2

A   B   E   C#
And you, you always told me, no matter how long it holds me,
   A   B   E
If it falls apart or makes us million - aires,
   A   B   E   C#m
You'll be right here for - ever, go through this thing to - gether,
   A   B   E
And on heaven's golden shore we'll lay our heads.

Interlude 2

As Interlude 1

Outro

    Emaj7   B9
Mmm.
    Emaj7   B9
Ah._____
    Emaj7   B9
Ah._____
    Emaj7   B9
Ah._____
    Emaj7   B9
Ah._____
    Emaj7   B9
Ah._____
    Emaj7   B9   Emaj7
Ah._____

The Greatest

Words & Music by
Chan Marshall

Intro

‖: C | Am | Em | Em :‖

Verse 1

    C   Am   Em
Once I wanted to be   the greatest,

    C   Am   Em
No wind or waterfall could stall me.

        F   Dm   G
And then came the rush of the flood,

The stars at night turned deep to dust.

Verse 2

(G)   C   Am   Em
Melt me down into big black armour,

           C   Am   Em
Leave no trace of grace, just in your honour.

           C   Am
Lower me down to culprit south,

Em
    Make 'em wash a space in town.

         F   Dm   G
For the lead and the dregs of my bed I've been sleeping.

         F   Dm
Lower me down, pin me in,

         G   C   Am Em
Secure the grounds for the later pa - rade.

Verse 3

C   Am   Em
Once I wanted to be   the greatest,

C   Am Em
Two fists of solid rock

C   Am   Em
With brains that could explain any   feeling.

         F   Dm   G
Lower me down, pin me in, secure the grounds

         F   Dm   G
For the lead and the dregs of my bed I've been sleeping.

              (C)
For the later pa - rade.

Link   ‖: C | Am | Em | Em :‖

Verse 4

C   Am   Em
Once I   wanted to be the greatest,

C   Am   Em
No wind or waterfall could stall me.

        F   Dm   G
And then came the rush of the flood,

                              F Dm G
The stars at night turned deep to dust.

He Doesn't Know Why

Words & Music by
Robin Pecknold

C   F   G   Dm   Am

Em   G⁷sus⁴   Fmaj⁷   B♭   Gsus⁴

Capo first fret

Intro

C (Dm) (Em) (F)
Ah._____

C (Dm) (Em) (F)
Ah._____

Verse 1

F   G   F   G
Penniless and tired with your hair grown long,

      Dm   Am   Em   F
I was looking at you there and your face looked wrong.

      C   Dm Em   F
Memo - ry is a fickle siren's song,

  G⁷sus⁴   G
I didn't understand.

Verse 2

F   G   F   G
In the gentle light as the morning nears,

      Dm   Am   Em   F
You don't say a single word of your last two years.

       C   Dm   Em   F
Where you were or when you reached the front - ier,

 G⁷sus⁴   G
I didn't understand,__ no.

Link 1

C (Dm) (Em) (F)
Ah._____

C (Dm) (Em) (F)
Ah._____

Verse 3

    F   **G**   **F**   **G**
See your rugged hands and a silver knife,
           Dm   **Am**   **Em**   **F**
Twenty dollars in your hand that you hold so tight.
         C   **Dm** **Em**   **F**
All the evidence of your vagrant life,
   G⁷sus⁴   **G**
My brother you were born.___

Verse 4

     F   **G**   **F**   **G**
And you will try to do what you did be - fore,
        Dm   **Am**   **Em**   **F**
Pull the wool over your eyes for a week or more.
        C   **Dm** **Em**   **F**
Let your family take you back to your
   G⁷sus⁴   **G**
O - riginal mind.___

Bridge

(G)   **C**
There's nothing I can do,
       Fmaj⁷   **C**
There's nothing I can do.

There's nothing I can say,
       Fmaj⁷   **C**
There's nothing I can say,

I can say.

Link 2

C **(Dm)** **(Em)** **(F)**
Ah._____
C **(Dm)** **(Em)** **(F)**
Ah._____
C **(Dm)** **(Em)** **(F)**
Ah._____
C **(Dm)** **(Em)** **(F)** **C**
Ah._____

Piano outro

| **F** | **F** | **C** | **C** | |

| **B♭** | **B♭** | **Gsus⁴** | **Gsus⁴** | **F** | ‖

The High Road

Words & Music by
James Mercer & Brian Burton

Dm   C   G   F   Am

Intro   ‖: Dm | C | G | G :‖ *Play 4 times*

Verse 1

    Dm   C   Dm
  We're bound to wait all night,
        C   Dm
She's bound to run amok.
      C   G
In - vested enough in it anyhow,
              Dm
To each his own.
      C   Dm
The garden needs sorting out,
      C   Dm
She curls her lips on the bow,
      C   G
And I don't know if I'm dead or not to anyone.

Chorus 1

Dm   C   Dm
  Come on and get the mini - mum,
      C   Dm
Be - fore you open up your eyes.
      C   G
This army has so many heads to analyse
Dm   C   Dm
  Come on and get your over - dose,
      C   Dm
Col - lect it at the border - line,
      C
And they want to get up in your head.

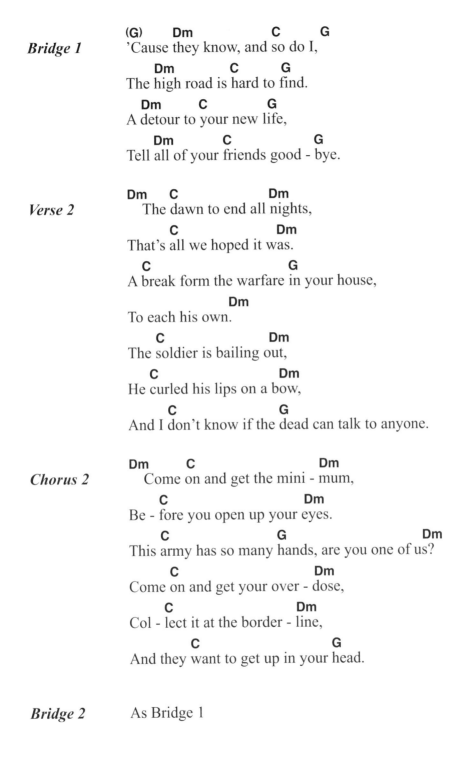

Bridge 1

(G)   Dm   C   G
'Cause they know, and so do I,

          Dm   C   G
The high road is hard to find.

        Dm   C   G
A detour to your new life,

        Dm   C   G
Tell all of your friends good - bye.

Verse 2

Dm   C   Dm
  The dawn to end all nights,

          C   Dm
That's all we hoped it was.

        C   G
A break form the warfare in your house,

                Dm
To each his own.

        C   Dm
The soldier is bailing out,

        C   Dm
He curled his lips on a bow,

        C   G
And I don't know if the dead can talk to anyone.

Chorus 2

Dm   C   Dm
  Come on and get the mini - mum,

        C   Dm
Be - fore you open up your eyes.

          C   G   Dm
This army has so many hands, are you one of us?

          C   Dm
Come on and get your over - dose,

        C   Dm
Col - lect it at the border - line,

            C   G
And they want to get up in your head.

Bridge 2   As Bridge 1

87

Link | F G | Dm | F G | Am G ‖

Outro

C   F
It's too late to change your mind,

      Dm   G
You let loss be your guide.

C   F
It's too late to change your mind,

      Dm   G
You let loss be your guide.

C   F
It's too late to change your mind,

      Dm   G
You let loss be your guide.

C   F
It's too late to change your mind,

      Dm   G
You let loss be your guide.

José González

Heartbeats

Words & Music by
Olof Dreijer & Karin Dreijer Andersson

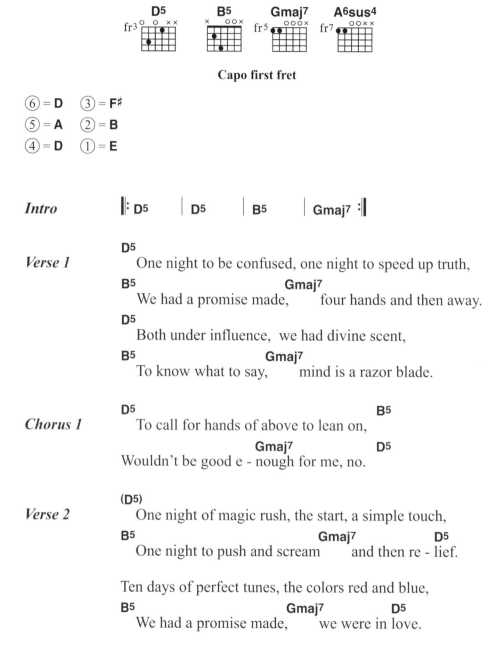

Capo first fret

⑥ = D ③ = F♯
⑤ = A ② = B
④ = D ① = E

Intro   ‖: D5 │ D5 │ B5 │ Gmaj7 :‖

Verse 1

D5
One night to be confused, one night to speed up truth,
B5   Gmaj7
We had a promise made,   four hands and then away.
D5
Both under influence, we had divine scent,
B5   Gmaj7
To know what to say,   mind is a razor blade.

Chorus 1

D5   B5
To call for hands of above to lean on,
                              Gmaj7   D5
Wouldn't be good e - nough for me, no.

Verse 2

(D5)
One night of magic rush, the start, a simple touch,
B5   Gmaj7   D5
One night to push and scream   and then re - lief.

Ten days of perfect tunes, the colors red and blue,
B5   Gmaj7   D5
We had a promise made,   we were in love.

Chorus 2

(**D5**)   **B5**
To call for hands of above to lean on,
                    Gmaj7   **D5**
Wouldn't be good e - nough for me, no.
                                        B5
To call for hands of above to lean on,
                    Gmaj7
Wouldn't be good e - nough.

Bridge

          A6sus4   **Gmaj7**
And you, you knew the hand of the devil,
          A6sus4   **Gmaj7**
And you, kept us awake with wolves' teeth.
                              B5
Sharing different heartbeats in one night.

Chorus 3

D5   **B5**
    To call for hands of above to lean on,
                    Gmaj7   **D5**
Wouldn't be good e - nough for me, no.
                              B5
To call for hands of above to lean on,
                    Gmaj7   **D5**
Wouldn't be good e - nough.

Hustle

Words & Music by
Michael Lindsay, Ben Bickerton, Martin Smith,
Rebecca Jacobs, Philip Winter & Ashley Bates

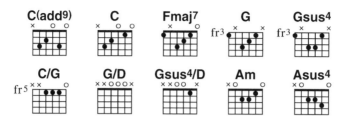

Capo second fret

Play 6 times

Intro

C(add9) C ‖: Fmaj7 | G Gsus4 G | C/G G/D Gsus4/D | C C(add9) C :‖

| Fmaj7 | G Gsus4 G | C/G G/D Gsus4/D | Am Asus4 Am |

| Fmaj7 | G Gsus4 G | C | C ‖

Verse 1

N.C.(C)   Fmaj7   G   C
When I come home, you won't be there any more,

        Fmaj7   G   C
When I come home, you won't be there any more.

          Fmaj7   G   C   Am
And you will tear off your clothes and kiss the floor,

         Fmaj7 G   C
When I come home, home, home.

Verse 2

      C(add9) C Fmaj7   G   Gsus4 G C/G   G/D Gsus4/D C
When I   see land you will conjure up   a storm,

      C(add9) C Fmaj7   G   Gsus4 G C/G   G/D Gsus4/D C
When I   see land you will conjure up   a storm.

    C(add9) C Fmaj7 G   Gsus4 G C/G   Am
And I   will tie your hands to   the highest mast,

    Asus4 Am Fmaj7 G   Gsus4 G
When I   see land, land,   land.

Chorus 1

(C)   **Fmaj⁷**   **G**   **C**
And we will hustle, hustle, hustle to be free,

        Fmaj⁷   **G**   **C**
Free from all the happy thoughts and smiles across the sea.

        Fmaj⁷   **G**
In favour of the mean, mean, moves

    C   **Am**   **Fmaj⁷**   **G**   **C**
And back doors to the heart from where we always, al - ways fall a - part.

Link

‖: **Fmaj⁷** | **G** | **C** | **C**   :‖

Verse 3

N.C.(C)   **Fmaj⁷**   **G**   **C**
And you will slide on the back of my bike,

       Fmaj⁷   **G**   **C**
And you will slide on the back seat of my bike.

      Fmaj⁷ **G** **C**   **Am**
And I will ride you home drunken in the rain,

      Fmaj⁷ **G**   **C**
'Cause you will win a - gain and a - gain.

Verse 4

(C)   **Fmaj⁷**   **G**   **C**
When it's your turn you will tie me to the tree,

      Fmaj⁷   **G**   **C**
Now it's your turn and you will tie me to the tree.

      Fmaj⁷ **G** **C**   **Am**
And you will sing and sing for - ever you and me,

      Fmaj⁷ **G**   **C**
And in the dark I wonder what you see.

Chorus 2   As Chorus 1

Chorus 3   As Chorus 1

Outro

‖: **Fmaj⁷** | **G** | **C** | **C**   :‖ *Play 3 times*

| **Fmaj⁷** | **G** | **C** | **C G C**‖

I Really Need Love

Words & Music by
Paul Fletcher, Aaron Fletcher, Timothy Parkin & Kris Birkin

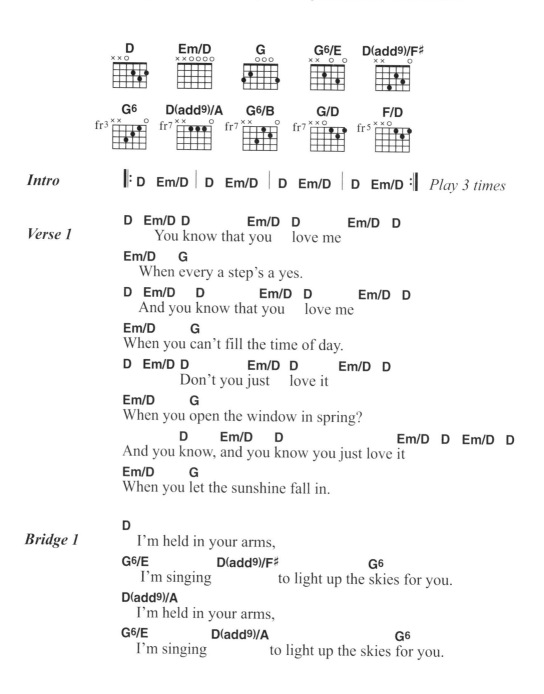

Intro

‖: D Em/D | D Em/D | D Em/D | D Em/D :‖ *Play 3 times*

Verse 1

D Em/D D   Em/D D   Em/D D
　　　You know that you   love me

Em/D   G
　When every a step's a yes.

D Em/D   D   Em/D D   Em/D D
　And you know that you   love me

Em/D   G
When you can't fill the time of day.

D Em/D D   Em/D D   Em/D D
　　　Don't you just   love it

Em/D   G
When you open the window in spring?

　　　　　　D   Em/D   D   Em/D D Em/D D
And you know, and you know you just love it

Em/D   G
When you let the sunshine fall in.

Bridge 1

D
　　I'm held in your arms,

G6/E   D(add9)/F♯   G6
　I'm singing   to light up the skies for you.

D(add9)/A
　I'm held in your arms,

G6/E   D(add9)/A   G6
　I'm singing   to light up the skies for you.

Link   ‖ D Em/D | D Em/D | D Em/D | D Em/D ‖

Verse 2

D Em/D D   Em/D D   Em D
     I don't wan - na   fool no more

Em/D G
On the goodness that there is.

D Em/D   D   Em/D D   Em/D D
  And I ain't fooling any - one

Em/D G
On the chances that there are to this.

       D   Em/D D   Em/D D   Em/D D
And I wish,   mmm, that love will   come

Em/D G
For   each and everyone.

       D   Em/D D   Em/D D   Em/D D
And I know   I'm gon - na   get me some

Em/D G
In the shadow of the sun.

Bridge 2

D   G6/B
  Don't wanna put my feelings

        D(add9)/F♯   G6
Into an - other song for you.

       D(add9)/A   G6/B
Oh, I don't want to put my feelings

       D(add9)/A   G6
Into an - other song, oh, because of you.

Chorus 1

(G6)   D   Em/D D   Em/D
Well, I really need love now, I really need love now,

 D   Em/D D   Em/D
I really need love now, I really need love now,

G
Really need love, really need love,

Really need love, really need love.

D   Em/D D   Em/D
Really need love now, really need love now,

D   Em/D D   Em/D
Really need love now, really need love oh,

G
Really need love, really need love,

Really need love, really need love.

95

cont.

```
D              Em/D  D              Em/D
```
Really need love now,   really need love now,
```
D              Em/D  D              Em/D
```
Really need love now,   really need love oh,
```
G
```
Really need love, really need love,

Really need love, really need love.
```
D              Em/D  D              Em/D
```
Really need love now,   really need love now,
```
D              Em/D  D              Em/D
```
Really need love now,   really need love oh,
```
G
```
Really need love, really need love,
```
                        (D)
```
Really need love, really need love.

Interlude   ‖: D   G/D ｜ F/D G/D ｜ D   G/D ｜ F/D   :‖ *Play 6 times*

Verse 3
```
D  Em/D  D          Em/D  D   Em/D  D
```
      You make me feel so   fun
```
Em/D       G
```
When I'm dancing on my way home.
```
D  Em/D  D              Em/D  D      Em/D  D
```
      You make me feel so   young
```
Em/D       G
```
When the morning, when the morning comes.
```
D  Em/D  D         Em/D  D        Em/D  D
```
      I'm thinking of   asking you
```
      Em/D   G
```
Oh, but you haven't even heard of me.
```
       D    Em/D  D    Em/D  D              Em/D  D
```
And I pray, I   want to   kiss you soon,
```
Em/D        G
```
'Cause this feeling, understand, yeah, yeah.

Chorus 2

     D
I really need love now, I really need love now,

I really need love now, I really need love now,
             Em/D D   **Em/D**
I really need love now, I really need love now,
     D   **Em/D D**   **Em/D**
I really need love now, I really need love now,
     D   **Em/D D**   **Em/D**
I really need love now, I really need love now,
     D   **Em/D D**   **Em/D**
I really need love now, I really need love now,
     D   **Em/D D**   **Em/D**
I really need love now, I really need love now,
     D   **Em/D D**   **Em/D**
I really need love now, I really need love now,
G
Really need love, really need love,

Really need love, I really need love now.

Chorus 3

     D   **Em/D D**   **Em/D**
𝄆 I really need love now, I really need love now,
     D   **Em/D D**   **Em/D**
I really need love now, I really need love now,
G
Really need love, really need love,

Really need love, really need love. 𝄇 *Repeat ad lib. 5 times to fade*

I Wanna Go To Marz

Words & Music by
John Grant

Bm   A   Em   B   F#m   E   F#

Capo first fret

Intro

| Bm | Bm | A | A |
| Em | Em | Bm | Bm ‖

Verse 1

Bm   A
Bittersweet, strawberry, marshmallow, butter - scotch,
Em   Bm
Polar bear, cashew, dixieland, phosphate, chocolate.

                                                        A
Lime tutti-frutti, special raspberry, leave it to me,

                                                        Bm
Three grace scotch lassie, cherry smash, lemon freeze.

Chorus 1

B   F#m
  I wanna go to Marz where   green rivers flow,
              A   E
And your sweet sixteen is waiting for you after the show.
Bm   F#
  I wanna go to Marz, you'll meet the gold dust twins tonight,
                    A   E
You'll get your heart's desire, I will meet you under the lights.

Link

| Bm | Bm | A | A |
| Em | Em | Bm | Bm ‖

Verse 2

Bm   A
Golden champagne, juicy grapefruit, lucky Mon - day,

Em   Bm
High school football, hot fudge, buffalo tulip sundae.

            A
Almond caramel frappe, pineapple root - beer,

Em   Bm
Black and white penny-apple, Henry Ford, sweetheart maple tea.

Chorus 2 As Chorus 1

Outro

Bm	Bm	F♯	F♯	
A	A	E	E	
Bm	Bm	F♯m	F♯m	
A	A	E	E	
Bm	Bm	F♯	F♯	
A	A	E	E	
Bm	Bm	F♯	F♯	
A	A	E	E	Bm ‖

99

I'd Rather Dance With You

Words & Music by
Erlend Øye & Eirik Glambek Bøe

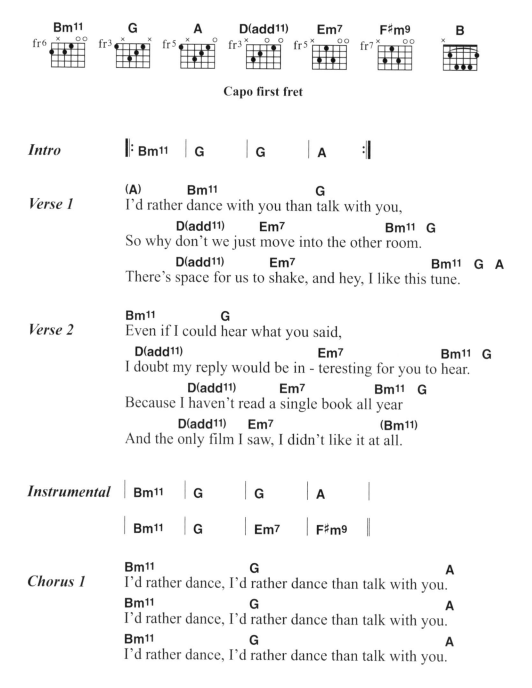

Capo first fret

Intro   ‖: Bm¹¹ | G | G | A :‖

Verse 1
(A)   Bm¹¹   G
I'd rather dance with you than talk with you,
          D(add¹¹)   Em⁷   Bm¹¹ G
So why don't we just move into the other room.
          D(add¹¹)   Em⁷   Bm¹¹ G A
There's space for us to shake, and hey, I like this tune.

Verse 2
Bm¹¹   G
Even if I could hear what you said,
      D(add¹¹)   Em⁷   Bm¹¹ G
I doubt my reply would be in - teresting for you to hear.
              D(add¹¹)   Em⁷   Bm¹¹ G
Because I haven't read a single book all year
              D(add¹¹)   Em⁷   (Bm¹¹)
And the only film I saw, I didn't like it at all.

Instrumental | Bm¹¹ | G | G | A |

| Bm¹¹ | G | Em⁷ | F♯m⁹ ‖

Chorus 1
Bm¹¹   G   A
I'd rather dance, I'd rather dance than talk with you.
Bm¹¹   G   A
I'd rather dance, I'd rather dance than talk with you.
Bm¹¹   G   A
I'd rather dance, I'd rather dance than talk with you.

Link 1 | Bm¹¹ | G | G | A   ‖

Bridge
      Bm¹¹
The music's too loud and the noise from the crowd
                       A
Increases the chance of misinterpretation.

Verse 3
      Bm¹¹   **G**
So let your hips do the talking,
       D(add¹¹)   **Em⁷**   **Bm¹¹** **G**
I'll make you laugh by acting like the guy who sings
       D(add¹¹)   **Em⁷**   **Bm¹¹** **G**
And you'll make me smile by really getting into the swing.
               G
Getting into the swing, getting into the swing.
               A   **Bm¹¹**
Getting into the swing, getting into the swing.
               G   **Em⁷**
Getting into the swing, getting into the swing.
             F♯m⁹   **Bm¹¹**
Getting into the swing, getting into the swing.

Chorus 2
Bm¹¹   **G**   **A**
I'd rather dance, I'd rather dance than talk with you.
Bm¹¹   **G**   **A**
I'd rather dance, I'd rather dance than talk with you.
Bm¹¹   **G**   **A**
I'd rather dance, I'd rather dance than talk with you.
Bm¹¹   **G**   **A**
I'd rather dance, I'd rather dance than talk with you.

   | Bm¹¹ | G | G | A |

   | Bm¹¹ | G | Em⁷ | F♯m⁹ |
                                   I'd rather dance with you.

   | Bm¹¹ | G | G | A |
                                     I'd rather dance with you.

   | Bm¹¹ | G | G | A   ‖

Outro | Bm¹¹ | G | G | A |

          | Bm¹¹ | G | Em⁷ | F♯m⁹ | B   ‖

In The Sun

Words & Music by
Joseph Arthur

Em7   Cmaj7   G   G5/F#   Cadd9

Capo third fret

Verse 1

Em7   Cmaj7
  I picture you in the sun

G   G5/F#
Wondering what went wrong

Em7   Cmaj7
  And falling down on your knees

G   G5/F#
Asking for sympathy

Em7   Cmaj7
  And being caught in between

G   G5/F#
All you wish for, and all you seem

Em7   Cmaj7
  And trying to find anything

G   G5/F#   Em7
You can't feel that you can be - lieve in.___

Chorus 1

(Em7) Cmaj7   G   G5/F#
        May God's love be with you

Em7   Cmaj7
Always___

                G   G5/F#
May God's love be with you.___

Verse 2

Em7   Cmaj7
 I know I would a - pologise

G   G5/F♯
If I could see your eyes

Em7   Cmaj7
 'Cause when you showed me myself

     G   G5/F♯
You know_ I became_ someone else

Em7   Cmaj7
 But I was caught in between

G   G5/F♯
All you wish for and all you need

Em7   Cmaj7
 I picture you fast asleep

  G   G5/F♯   Em7
A night that comes, you can't keep a - wake._

Chorus 2

(Em7) Cmaj7   G   G5/F♯
      May God's love be with you_

 Em7 Cmaj7
𝄆 Always__

    G   G5/F♯
May God's love be with you._ 𝄇 *Play 3 times*

Bridge 1

Cadd9   G
 'Cause if I find, if I find my way

G5/F♯   Cadd9
How much will I find?

      G
If I find, if I find my way

G5/F♯   Cadd9
How much will I find?

      G
If I find, if I find my way

G5/F♯   Em7 Cmaj7
How much will I find?_(you)

   G G5/F♯
Yeah_

   Em7 Cmaj7
I'll find_ you_

   G G5/F♯
Yeah, yeah._

| Em7 | Cmaj7 | G | G5/F♯ ‖

Verse 3

Em7   Cmaj7
   Oh, I don't know anymore

G   G5/F♯   Em7
What it's for, I'm not even sure

       Cmaj7   G
If there is anyone who is in the sun

     G5/F♯   Em7
Will you help me to under - stand?

          Cmaj7
'Cause I've been caught in between

G   G5/F♯
All I wish for and all I need

Em7   Cmaj7
  Or maybe you're not even sure

G   G5/F♯   Em7
What it's for any more than me.___

Chorus 3

(Em7) Cmaj7   G   G5/F♯
       May God's love be with you

Em7   Cmaj7
Always___

      G   G5/F♯
May God's love be with you

Em7   Cmaj7
Always___

      G   G5/F♯
May God's love be with you

Em7   Cmaj7
Always___

      G   G5/F♯
May God's love be with you.___

Bridge 2

Cadd9   G
   'Cause if I find, if I find my way

G5/F♯   Cadd9
How much will I find?

                G
If I find, if I find my way

G5/F♯   Cadd9
How much will I find?

                G
If I find, if I find my way

G5/F♯   Cadd9
How much will I find?

                G
If I find, if I find my way

G5/F♯   Em7   Cmaj7
How much will I find?__(you)

      G   G5/F♯
Yeah, yeah__

     Em7   Cmaj7
I'll find__you

      G   G5/F♯
Yeah, yeah____

     Em7   Cmaj7
I'll find__you

      G   G5/F♯
Yeah, yeah.____

Outro   ‖: Em7 | Cmaj7 | G5 | G5/F♯ :‖ Em7   ‖

Ivy & Gold

Words & Music by
Jack Steadman

G   Cmaj⁷   Am   Em   D   Dm   C   G%

Capo sixth fret

Intro | G | Cmaj⁷ | G | Am |

            | G | Em | G D | G   ‖

Verse 1

```
G                            Cmaj⁷
Waking sitting upright, can't explain the sunlight
G                      Am
Wondering why you're not home.
G                      Em
Then I'll go beside you, left before you tried to
G       D        G
Work out all the un - knowns.
```

Verse 2

```
G                            Cmaj⁷
Blame it all on me when I forget to defend
G                      Am
Everything that we worked out.
G                      Em
Something in her wording, I cannot help searching
G       D        G
For what memory found.
```

Chorus 1

```
Dm                                        C          (G)
   Thought it stopped just as it start, but that is not what you are.
```

| G | Em | G D | G |

```
Dm                                   C      (G)
   You're a layer on my clothes made of ivy and gold.
```

Link	| G	| Cmaj⁷	| G	| Am	|
	| G	| Em	| G D	| G	||

Verse 3

```
G                         Cmaj⁷
Meet me in the hallway, bite your lip when I say
G                            Am
Never have you left my mind.
G                          Em
Stop and think it over, smile and move in closer,
G        D        G
Oh what delicate time.
```

Verse 4

```
G                         Cmaj⁷
Blame it all on me when I forget to defend
G                          Am
Everything that we put down.
G                           Em
Something in her wording, I guess she was just searching
G        D        G
For some monetary sound.
```

Chorus 2

```
Dm                                          C              (G)
    Thought it stopped just as it start, but that is not what you are.
```

| G	| Em	| G D	| G	|

```
Dm                                   C         (G)
   You're a layer on my clothes made of ivy and gold.
```

| G	| Em	| G D	| G	|

```
Dm                                   C         (G)
You're a layer on my clothes made of ivy and gold.
```

Outro	| G	| Cmaj⁷	| G	| Am	|
	| G	| Em	| G D	| G	| G‰	||

John Wayne Gacy, Jr.

Words & Music by
Sufjan Stevens

Dm   **C(add9)**   **Am**   **Fmaj7**

Capo third fret

Intro   ‖: Dm | C(add9) | Am | Fmaj7 :‖

Verse 1

Dm   C(add9)
  His father was a drinker
      Am   Fmaj7
And his mother cried in bed.
Dm   C(add9)
  Folding John Wayne's t-shirts
        Am   Fmaj7
When the swing-set hit his head.
Dm   C(add9)
  The neighbours they a - dored him
      Am   Fmaj7
For his humour and his   conversation.
Dm   C(add9)
  Look underneath the house there,
      Am
Find the few living things,
      Fmaj7   Dm
Rotting fast, in their sleep, oh the dead.
        C(add9)
Twenty-seven people,
      Am
Even more, they were boys
       Fmaj7   Dm   C(add9)
With their cars, summer jobs, oh my God,_____
Am   Fmaj7
Ooh, are you one of them?

Verse 2

Dm   C(add9)
   He dressed up like a clown for them

      Am   Fmaj7
With his face paint white and red.

Dm   C(add9)
   And on his best be - haviour

      Am   Fmaj7   Dm
In a dark room on the bed he kissed them all.

                  C(add9)
He'd kill ten thousand people

      Am   Fmaj7   Dm
With a sleight of his hand running far, running fast to the dead.

              C(add9)
He took off all their clothes for them,

      Am
He put a cloth on their lips,

    Fmaj7   Dm   C(add9) Am Fmaj7
Quiet hands, quiet kiss on the mouth._____

Dm   C(add9)
   And in my best be - haviour,

      Am   Fmaj7
I am really just like him.

Dm   C(add9)
   Look beneath the floorboards

      Am   Fmaj7
For the secrets I have hid.

Jolene

Words & Music by
Ray LaMontagne

G   C/G   Csus2/G   C   C(add9)   Em

D   Dsus4   G/B   Am   Am11   G7   G/F#

Intro ‖: G | C/G | Csus2/G | C/G :‖

Verse 1
```
G          C        G
Cocaine flame in my bloodstream,
                      C        C(add9)
Sold my coat when I hit   Spokane.
C                                              G C/G C
Bought myself a hard pack of cigarettes in the early morning rain.

Lately my hands they don't feel like mine,
                  C                      C(add9)  C
My eyes been stung with dust and blind.
                                              G
Held you in my arms one time, lost you just the same.
```

Chorus 1
```
Em   G   C      G   D   Em      G   C
 Jo - lene   I ain't a - bout to go    straight, it's too late.
G            C        G
I found myself face down in a ditch,
D                Dsus4         D
Booze in my hair, blood on my lips,
  C
A picture of you holding a picture of me
                            G
In the pocket of my blue jeans.
Em          G          C        C(add9)
 Still don't know what love means,
Em          G          C        G/B Am Am11 C G/B Am
 Still don't know what love means
     G        C   G/B   Am
Jo - lene, la la la la la la la,
   (G)
Jo - lene.
```

Link 1 ‖: G | C/G | Csus2/G | C/G   :‖

Verse 2

G
Been so long since I seen your face
      G7   C
Or felt a part of this human race,
                                              G C/G G
I've been living out of this here suitcase for way too long.

A man needs something he can hold onto,
             G7   C
A nine-pound hammer or a woman like you,
                        G G/F♯
Either one of them things will do.

Chorus 2

    Em   G   C   G   D   Em   G   C
   Jo - lene   I ain't a - bout to go   straight, it's too late.
G   C   G
I found myself face down in a ditch,
D   Dsus4   D
Booze in my hair, blood on my lips,
     C
A picture of you holding a picture of me
                      G   G/F♯
In the pocket of my blue jeans.
Em   G   C   C(add9)
   Still don't know what love means,
Em   G   C   G/B Am Am11 C G/B Am
   Still don't know what love means
    G   C G/B   Am
Jo - lene, la la la la la la la,
     G   C G/B   Am
Jo - lene, la la la la la la la,
   (G)
Jo - lene.

Outro ‖: G | C/G | Csus2/G | C/G   :‖

The King Of Carrot Flowers
(Part One)

Words & Music by
Jeff Mangum

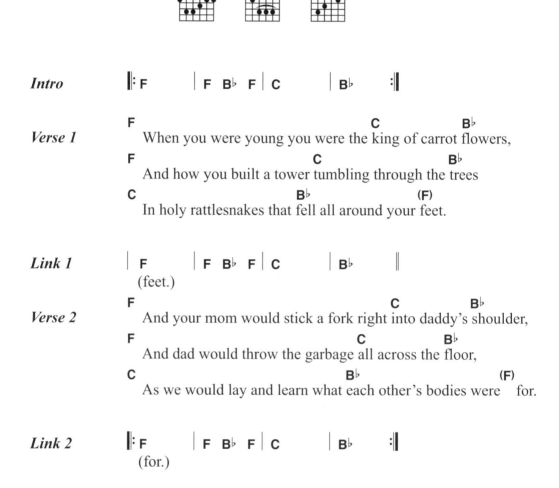

Intro ‖: F | F B♭ F | C | B♭ :‖

Verse 1

F   C   B♭
When you were young you were the king of carrot flowers,

F   C   B♭
And how you built a tower tumbling through the trees

C   B♭   (F)
In holy rattlesnakes that fell all around your feet.

Link 1 | F | F B♭ F | C | B♭ ‖

(feet.)

Verse 2

F   C   B♭
And your mom would stick a fork right into daddy's shoulder,

F   C   B♭
And dad would throw the garbage all across the floor,

C   B♭   (F)
As we would lay and learn what each other's bodies were   for.

Link 2 ‖: F | F B♭ F | C | B♭ :‖

(for.)

Verse 3

F   C   Bb
And this is the room one after - noon I knew I could love you,

F   C   Bb
And from above you how I sank into your soul,

C   Bb   (F)
Into that secret place where no one dares to   go.

Link 3 | F | F Bb F | C | Bb ||
(go.)

Verse 4

F   C   Bb
And your mom would drink until she was no longer speaking,

F   C   Bb
And dad would dream of all the different ways to die,

C   Bb   F   Bb F C Bb F Bb F
Each one a little more than he could dare to try._____

C   Bb F Bb F
Ay._____

C   Bb F Bb F
Ay._____

C   Bb F
Ay._____

La Ritournelle

Words & Music by
Sébastien Tellier

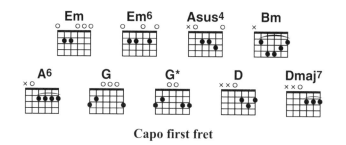

Capo first fret

Intro

| 𝄆 Em | Em6 | Asus4 | Bm | A6 𝄇 *Play 4 times* |

| G | G* | D | Dmaj7 | |

| G | G* | Bm | A6 | A6 | |

| 𝄆 Em | Em6 | Asus4 | Bm | A6 𝄇 |

| 𝄆 G | Em | Bm | A6 𝄇 |

| A6 | Em | Em | G | Asus4 |

| Bm | Bm | Bm | Bm | 𝄂 |

Verse

Em
Nothing's gonna change my love for you.

Em6   **Asus4**   **Bm**   **A6**
  I wanna spend my life with you,

        Em
So we'll make love on the grass under the moon.

Em6   **Asus4**   **Bm**   **A6**
  No one can tell, damned if I do.

cont.

         Em
Forever journey on golden avenues,

Em⁶   **Em**   **Asus⁴**   **Bm**   **A⁶**
    Drift in your eyes since I love you, oh.

Em⁶   **Asus⁴**
I've got beat in my veins for only rule,

Love is to share, mine is for you.

Outro   ‖: **Bm** | **A⁶** | **G** | **Em** :‖

            | **Bm** | **A⁶** | **A⁶** |

            ‖: **Em** | **Em⁶** | **Asus⁴** | **Bm** | **A⁶** :‖ *Play 4 times*

            ‖: **Em** | **Em⁶** | **Asus⁴** | **Bm** | **A⁶** :‖ *Slowing down*

            | **Em**   ‖

The Last Of The Melting Snow

Words & Music by
Nick Hemming

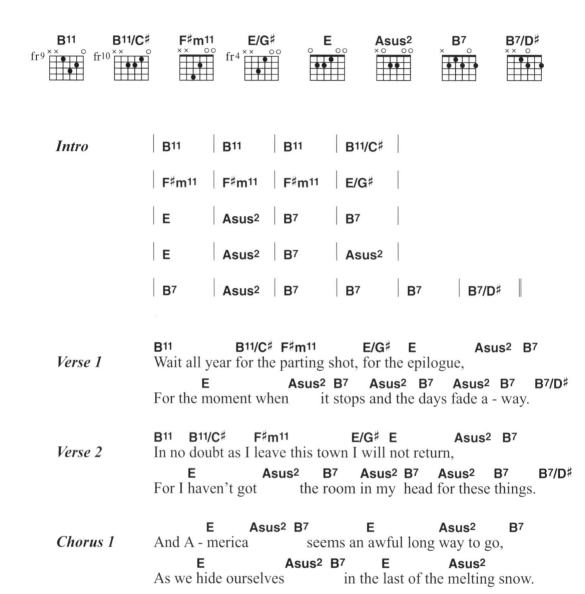

Intro | B11 | B11 | B11 | B11/C♯ |

| F♯m11 | F♯m11 | F♯m11 | E/G♯ |

| E | Asus2 | B7 | B7 |

| E | Asus2 | B7 | Asus2 |

| B7 | Asus2 | B7 | B7 | B7 | B7/D♯ ‖

Verse 1
B11   B11/C♯ F♯m11   E/G♯ E   Asus2 B7
Wait all year for the parting shot, for the epilogue,
         E   Asus2 B7   Asus2 B7 Asus2 B7   B7/D♯
For the moment when   it stops and the days fade a - way.

Verse 2
B11 B11/C♯   F♯m11   E/G♯ E   Asus2 B7
In no doubt as I leave this town I will not return,
       E   Asus2   B7   Asus2 B7 Asus2 B7   B7/D♯
For I haven't got   the room in my head for these things.

Chorus 1
        E   Asus2 B7   E   Asus2   B7
And A - merica   seems an awful long way to go,
      E   Asus2 B7   E   Asus2
As we hide ourselves   in the last of the melting snow.

Link | B7 | Asus2 | B7 | Asus2 |

| B7 | B7 | B7 | B7/D♯ ‖

Verse 3

B11   B11/C♯ F♯m11   E/G♯ E   Asus2 B7
So we find in the   fading light of the wintertime,

               E   Asus2   B7 Asus2 B7 Asus2 B7 B7/D♯
That there's nothing left   to try,   all is   best left un - said.

Chorus 2

            E   Asus2 B7   E   Asus2   B7
And A - merica   seems an awful long way to go,

         E   Asus2 B7   E   Asus2   B7
As we hide ourselves   in the last of the melting snow.

         E   Asus2   B7
In the last of the melting snow.

         E   Asus2
In the last of the melting snow.

Outro | B7 | Asus2 | B7 | Asus2 |

| B7 | B7 | B7   ‖

Little Lion Man

Words & Music by
Mumford & Sons

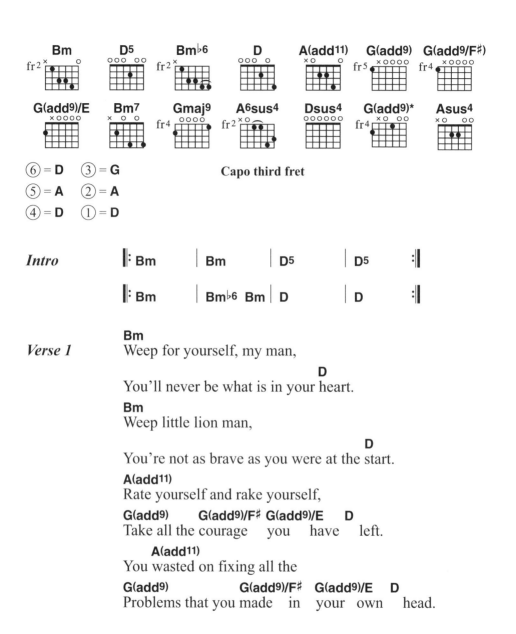

Capo third fret

Intro

‖: Bm | Bm | D5 | D5 :‖

‖: Bm | Bm♭6 Bm | D | D :‖

Verse 1

Bm
Weep for yourself, my man,

                                          D
You'll never be what is in your heart.

Bm
Weep little lion man,

                                                    D
You're not as brave as you were at the start.

A(add11)
Rate yourself and rake yourself,

G(add9)   G(add9)/F♯ G(add9)/E   D
Take all the courage   you   have   left.

         A(add11)
You wasted on fixing all the

G(add9)   G(add9)/F♯ G(add9)/E   D
Problems that you made   in   your   own   head.

Chorus 1

D   Bm⁷   Gmaj⁹   D
But it was not your fault but mine,

            Bm⁷   Gmaj⁹ D
And it was your heart on the line.

           Bm⁷   Gmaj⁹ D
I really fucked it up this time,

              A⁶sus⁴
Didn't I, my dear?

Didn't I, my?

Link 1

‖: Bm | Bm♭6 Bm | D | D   :‖

Verse 2

Bm
Tremble for yourself, my man,

   Bm♭6   Bm   D
You know that you have seen this all be - fore.

Bm
Tremble little lion man,

    Bm♭6   Bm   D
You'll never settle any of your scores.

     A(add¹¹)
Your grace is wasted in your face,

    G(add⁹)   G(add⁹)/F♯ G(add⁹)/E D
Your boldness stands a - lone   among the wreck.

    A(add¹¹)
Now learn from your mother or else

G(add⁹)   G(add⁹)/F♯ G(add⁹)/E D
Spend your days biting   your own   neck.

Chorus 2

D   Bm⁷   Gmaj⁹   D
But it was not your fault but mine,

            Bm⁷   Gmaj⁹ D
And it was your heart on the line.

        Bm⁷   Gmaj⁹ D
I really fucked it up this time,

              A⁶sus⁴
Didn't I, my dear?

Chorus 3

   D   Bm7   Gmaj9   D
But it was not your fault but mine,

             Bm7   Gmaj9 D
And it was your heart on the line.

        Bm7   Gmaj9 D
I really fucked it up this time,

              A6sus4
Didn't I, my dear?

            (Bm)
Didn't I, my dear?

Interlude

‖: Bm | Bm | D | D :‖ Dsus4 | D

| G(add9)* | G(add9)* | Asus4 | D5 | G(add9)* | G(add9)* |

Asus4 D5 G(add9)*
Ah._____

     Asus4 D5 G(add9)*
Ah._____

     Asus4 D5 G(add9)*
Ah._____

     Asus4 D5 G(add9)*
Ah._____

     Asus4 D5 G(add9)*
Ah._____

     Asus4 D5 G(add9)*
Ah._____

Chorus 4

G(add9)* Bm7   Gmaj9   D
But it was not your fault but mine,

            Bm7   Gmaj9 D
And it was your heart on the line.

        Bm7   Gmaj9 D
I really fucked it up this time,

              A6sus4
Didn't I, my dear?

         N.C.
But it was not your fault but mine,

And it was your heart on the line.

I really fucked it up this time,

Didn't I, my dear?

        D5
Didn't I, my dear?

Long Live The Queen

Words & Music by
Frank Turner

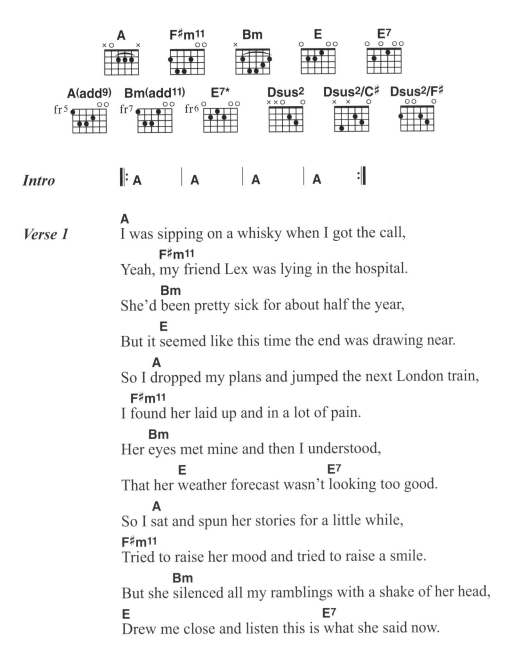

Intro ‖: A | A | A | A :‖

Verse 1

A
I was sipping on a whisky when I got the call,

F♯m11
Yeah, my friend Lex was lying in the hospital.

Bm
She'd been pretty sick for about half the year,

E
But it seemed like this time the end was drawing near.

A
So I dropped my plans and jumped the next London train,

F♯m11
I found her laid up and in a lot of pain.

Bm
Her eyes met mine and then I understood,

E   E7
That her weather forecast wasn't looking too good.

A
So I sat and spun her stories for a little while,

F♯m11
Tried to raise her mood and tried to raise a smile.

Bm
But she silenced all my ramblings with a shake of her head,

E   E7
Drew me close and listen this is what she said now.

Chorus 1

A(add9)   F♯m11   Bm(add11)

  You'll live to dance another day,

                           E7*

It's just now you'll have to dance for the two of us.

A(add9)   F♯m11   Bm(add11)

  So stop looking so damned de - pressed

                      Dsus2   E

And sing with all your heart that the Queen is dead.

Verse 2

E   A

Yeah, she told me she was sick of all the hospital food,

    F♯m11

And of doctors, distant relatives, draining her blood.

  Bm

She said, "I know I'm dying, but I'm not finished just yet,

     E

Yeah, I'm dying for a drink and for a cigarette."

    A

So we hatched a plan to book ourselves a cheap hotel,

   F♯m11

The centre of the city and to raise some hell

  Bm   E

Lay waste to all the clubs and then when everyone else

               E7   (A(add9))

Is long asleep then we'll know we're good and done.

Chorus 2

A(add9)   F♯m11   Bm(add11)

  You'll live to dance another day,

                           E7*

It's just now you'll have to dance for the two of us.

A(add9)   F♯m11   Bm(add11)

  So stop looking so damned de - pressed

                      Dsus2   E   Dsus2

And sing with all your heart that the Queen is dead.

Bridge

Dsus2 Dsus2/C♯ Bm   Dsus2 Dsus2/C♯ Bm

               And South London's not the same   any - more,

     Dsus2 Dsus2/C♯ Bm

The Queen is dead,_____

                   Dsus2   Dsus2/C♯   E7

And the last of the greats has finally gone to bed.

Verse 3

  (E7)   A(add9)
Well I was working on some words when Sarah called me up,

         F♯m11
She said that Lex had gone asleep and wasn't waking up.

     Bm
And even though I knew that there was nothing to be done,

     E   E7
I felt bad for not being there and now, well, she was gone.

A(add9)
So I tried to think what Lex would want me to do

     F♯m11
At times like this when I was feeling blue.

     Bm
So I gathered up some friends to spread the sad, sad news

      E   E7   A
And we headed to the city for a drink or two and we sang.

Chorus 3

A(add9)   F♯m11   Bm(add11)
  We live to dance another day,

                        E7*
It's just now we have to dance for one more of us.

A(add9)   F♯m11   Bm(add11)
  So stop looking so damned de - pressed

                       Dsus2 E   Dsus2/F♯
And sing with all our hearts, long live the Queen.

Lost Cause

Words & Music by
Beck Hansen

Fmaj7   C   Gadd11/B   Am   E7   G6   A7

Intro 𝄆 Fmaj7 | C   Gadd11/B 𝄇 *Play 4 times*

Verse 1

Fmaj7   C   Gadd11/B
Your sorry eyes

Fmaj7   C   Gadd11/B
Cut through the bone

Fmaj7   C   Gadd11/B
They make it hard

Am   E7
To leave you alone

Fmaj7   C   Gadd11/B
Leave you here

Fmaj7   C   Gadd11/B
Wearing your wounds

Fmaj7   C   Gadd11/B
Waving your guns

Am   E7
At somebody new.

Chorus 1

Fmaj7   G6
Baby you're lost

Fmaj7   G6
Baby you're lost

Fmaj7   G6   C
Baby you're a lost cause.

Verse 2

Fmaj7   C   Gadd11/B
There's too many people

Fmaj7   C   Gadd11/B
You used to know

Fmaj7   C   Gadd11/B
They see you coming

Am   E7
They see you go

cont.

```
Fmaj7              C              Gadd11/B
  They know your secrets
Fmaj7            C           Gadd11/B
  And you know theirs
Fmaj7          C             Gadd11/B
  This town is crazy;
Am        E7
  Nobody cares.
```

Chorus 2 As Chorus 1

Link 1 | A7 ||

Chorus 3

```
Fmaj7          G6
  I'm tired of fighting
Fmaj7          G6
  I'm tired of fighting
Fmaj7       G6                   C
            Fighting for a lost cause.
```

Bridge

```
A7          Fmaj7                C      Gadd11/B
  There's a place where you are going
A7          Fmaj7        C     Gadd11/B
  You ain't never been before
A7        Fmaj7             C            Gadd11/B
  No one left to watch your back now
Fmaj7                       C
  No one standing at your door
Fmaj7                            C
  That's what you thought love was for.
```

Chorus 4 As Chorus 1

Link 2 | A7 ||

Chorus 5 As Chorus 3

Outro | C | C | C | C (fermata) ||

The Most Beautiful Girl (In The Room)

Words & Music by
Jemaine Clement & Bret McKenzie

Dmaj7   Amaj7   Gmaj13/E   A13   A7   Amaj13   Dm(add9)/A

Intro

| N.C. | Dmaj7 | Amaj7 | Gmaj13/E | N.C. |

| Dmaj7 | Amaj7 | Gmaj13/E | A13 A7 |

| Dmaj7 | Amaj7 | Gmaj13/E |

Verse 1

N.C. Dmaj7   Amaj7
Yeah,   looking 'round the room,

          Gmaj13/E
I can tell that you

        Amaj7   A7   Dmaj7   Amaj7
Are the most beautiful girl in the   room,

Gmaj13/E   Amaj7 A7
  In the whole wide room. Ooh.

Dmaj7   Amaj7
  And when you're on the street,

          Gmaj13/E
Depending on the street,

       Amaj7   N.C.
I bet you are definitely in the top three.

Verse 2

Dmaj7   Amaj7   Gmaj13/E
Good looking girls on the street, yeah,

        Amaj7 A7
Depending on the street, ooh

Dmaj7   Amaj7
  And when I saw you at my mate's place,

      Amaj13
I thought what is she doing

    Dmaj7
At my mate's place,

Amaj7   Gmaj13/E   Amaj7
How did Dave get a hottie like that to a party like this?

cont.

A¹³   A⁷ Dmaj⁷
Good one Dave!

Amaj⁷   Gmaj¹³/E   Amaj⁷ A⁷
Ooh, you're a legend, Dave!

Verse 3

Dmaj⁷   Amaj⁷
I asked Dave if he's gonna make a move on you.

Gmaj¹³/E   Amaj⁷   A⁷   Dmaj⁷
He's not sure, I said "Dave do you mind if I do?"

**   Amaj⁷   Gmaj¹³/E**
He says he doesn't mind, but I can tell he kinda minds,

**   Amaj⁷   A⁷**
But I'm gonna do it anyway.

Dmaj⁷   Amaj⁷
I see you standing all a - lone by the stereo,

Gmaj¹³/E   Amaj⁷
I dim the lights down to very low, here we go.

Chorus 1

Dmaj⁷   Amaj⁷
You're so beautiful,

Gmaj¹³/E   Amaj⁷ A⁷
Well, you could be a waitress. Mmm.

Dmaj⁷   Amaj⁷
You're so beautiful,

Gmaj¹³/E   Amaj⁷ A⁷   Dmaj⁷
Well, you could be an air host - ess in the sixties.

**   Amaj⁷**
You're so beautiful,

Gma⁷¹³/E   Amaj⁷ A⁷ Dmaj⁷ Amaj⁷
Well, you could be a part - time model.

**   Gma¹³/E**
And then I seal the deal

**   Amaj⁷**
I do my moves, I do my dance moves.

Bridge

Amaj⁷   Dm(add⁹)/A
Ooh, feel my dance moves,

Amaj⁷ Dm(add⁹)/A
Mmm, ah, ah oh, ah, ah, oh.

Amaj⁷   Dm(add⁹)/A
It's twelve-o-two, just me and you

**   Amaj⁷**
And seven other dudes around you on the dance floor.

**   Dm(add⁹)/A**
I draw you near, "Let's get outta here,

**   Dmaj⁷**
Let's get in a cab, I'll buy you a ke - bab."

Verse 4

Dmaj7   Amaj7   Gmaj13/E
And I can't be - lieve that I'm sharing a kebab

       Amaj7 A7
With the most beautiful girl

     Dmaj7   Amaj7 Gmaj13/E
I have ever seen with a ke - bab. Ooh.

Dmaj7   Amaj7
 "Why don't we leave?

     Gmaj13/E   Amaj7   A7   Dmaj7
Let's go to my house and we can feel each other up on the couch."

     Amaj7   Gmaj13/E Amaj7 A7
Oh no. I don't mind taking it slow-ho-ho, no-ho-ho, yeah.

Chorus 2

Dmaj7   Amaj7
 'Cause you're so beautiful,

     Gmaj13/E   Amaj7 A7
Like a tree

         Dmaj7
Or a high-class prostitute.

       Amaj7
You're so beautiful,

Gmaj13/E   Amaj7 Bm7
 Mmm, you could be a part-time model.

Outro

Bm7   Dmaj7
 But you'd probably still have to keep your normal job

      Bm7
A part-time model,

      Dmaj7
Spending part of your time modelling

N.C.   Dmaj7 Amaj7 Gmaj13/E Amaj7
And part of your time, next to me._____

Dmaj7 Amaj7   Gmaj13/E   Amaj7   A7
  And the rest of the time doing your normal job.

Dmaj7 Amaj7
Ooh._____

Gmaj13/E   Amaj7 A7   Dmaj7 Amaj7 Gmaj13/E Amaj7 A7
 My place is usually tidier than this.

| Dmaj7 | Amaj7 | Gmaj13/E | Amaj7 ‖

128

Elliott Smith

Miss Misery

Words & Music by
Elliott Smith

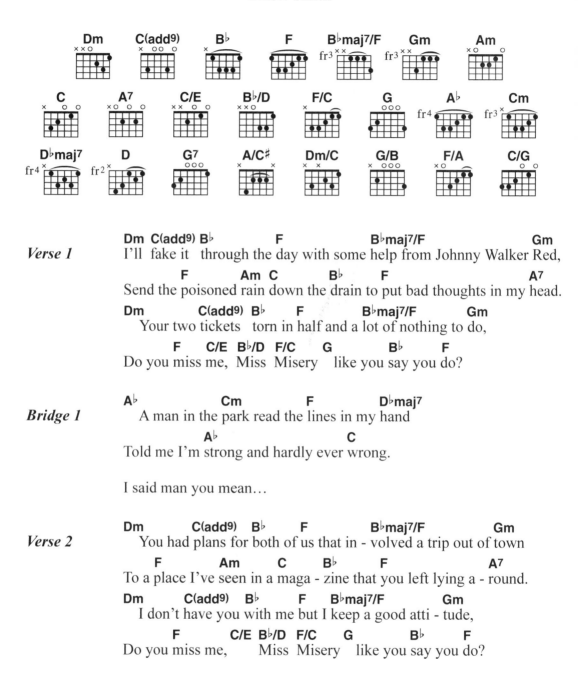

Verse 1

Dm C(add9) B♭   F   B♭maj7/F   Gm
I'll fake it through the day with some help from Johnny Walker Red,

     F   Am C   B♭   F   A7
Send the poisoned rain down the drain to put bad thoughts in my head.

Dm   C(add9) B♭   F   B♭maj7/F   Gm
     Your two tickets torn in half and a lot of nothing to do,

     F   C/E B♭/D F/C   G   B♭   F
Do you miss me, Miss Misery like you say you do?

Bridge 1

A♭   Cm   F   D♭maj7
     A man in the park read the lines in my hand

         A♭   C
Told me I'm strong and hardly ever wrong.

I said man you mean…

Verse 2

Dm   C(add9)   B♭   F   B♭maj7/F   Gm
     You had plans for both of us that in - volved a trip out of town

     F   Am   C   B♭   F   A7
To a place I've seen in a maga - zine that you left lying a - round.

Dm   C(add9)   B♭   F   B♭maj7/F   Gm
     I don't have you with me but I keep a good atti - tude,

     F   C/E B♭/D F/C   G   B♭   F
Do you miss me,   Miss Misery like you say you do?

Bridge 2

    D   **C** **B♭**
I know you'd rather see me gone
      F   **G7**   **B♭**
Than to see me the way that I am
                C   **A/C♯**
But I am in your life any - way.

Verse 3

Dm   **Dm/C** **B♭**   **F**   **B♭** **B♭maj7/F**   **Gm**
Next door the T.V.'s flashing blue frames on the wall,
   F   **Am**   **C**   **B♭**   **F**   **A7**
It's a come - dy of er - rors, you see, it's a - bout taking a fall.
Dm   **C(add9)** **B♭**   **F**   **B♭maj7/F**   **Gm**
To va - nish into   ob - livion   it's easy to do,
    F   **C/E**   **B♭/D**
And I try to be   but you know me
 F/C   **G/B**   **B♭**   **F/A C/G**
I   come back when you want me to.
       F   **C/E B♭/D F/C**   **G**   **B♭**   **F**
Do you miss me, Miss Misery like you say you do?

Mykonos

Words & Music by
Robin Pecknold

C#m/G# B/F# A/E G#m/D# A

C#m B6 A6 G#m F#m

Intro

‖: C#m/G# B/F# A/E G#m/D# | A/E A B/F# G#m/D# :‖

C#m B6 A6 G#m A6 G#m C#m
Oh._____

B6 A6 G#m A6 G#m C#m
Oh._____

Verse 1

C#m   B6   A6   B6   G#m   A6
The door slammed loud and rose up a cloud of dust on us.

C#m   B6   A6   B6   G#m   A6
Footsteps follow down through the hollow sound, torn up.

Chorus 1

F#m   C#m
And you will go to Myko - nos,

G#m   C#m
With a vision of the gentle coast,

F#m   C#m
And a sun to maybe dissi - pate,

G#m   A6   B6
Shadows of the mess you made.

Link 1

C#m B6 A6 G#m A6 G#m C#m
Oh._____

B6 A6 G#m A6 G#m C#m
Oh._____

Verse 2

C#m   B6 A6   B6   G#m   A6
How did any holes in the snow tipped pines, I find,

C#m   B6   A6   B6   G#m   A6
Hatching from the seed of your thin mind, all night?

Chorus 2   As Chorus 1

Link 2   As Link 1

| | C♯m/G♯ | B/F♯ | A/E | G♯m/D♯ | B6 |

Interlude
                         C♯m/G♯ B/F♯ A/E G♯m/D♯ B6
Ooh,___ Oh._____

                         C♯m/G♯ B/F♯ A/E G♯m/D♯ A6
Ooh,___ Oh._____

                         C♯m/G♯ B/F♯ A/E G♯m/D♯ B6
Ooh,___ Oh._____

N.C.
Ooh.___

Bridge 1
N.C. (C♯m)   (B6)   (A6)
Brother you don't need to turn me a - way,

(C♯m)   (B6)   (A6)
I was waiting down at the ancient gates.

F♯m   B6
  You go wher - ever you go today,

F♯m   B6
  You go to - day.

C♯m   B6   A6
  I remember how they took you down,

C♯m   B6   A6
  As the winter turned the meadow a - round.

F♯m   B6
  You go wher - ever you go today,

F♯m   B6
  You go to - day.

C♯m   B6   A6
  When I'm walking brother don't you for - get,

C♯m   B6   A6
  It ain't often that you'd ever find a friend,

F♯m   B6
  You go wher - ever you go today,

F♯m   B6
  You go to - day.

Outro
    F♯m   B6
‖:   You go wher - ever you go today,

F♯m   B6
  You go to - day. :‖ *Repeat to fade*

No One's Gonna Love You

Words & Music by
Benjamin Bridwell, James Hampton & Creighton Barrett

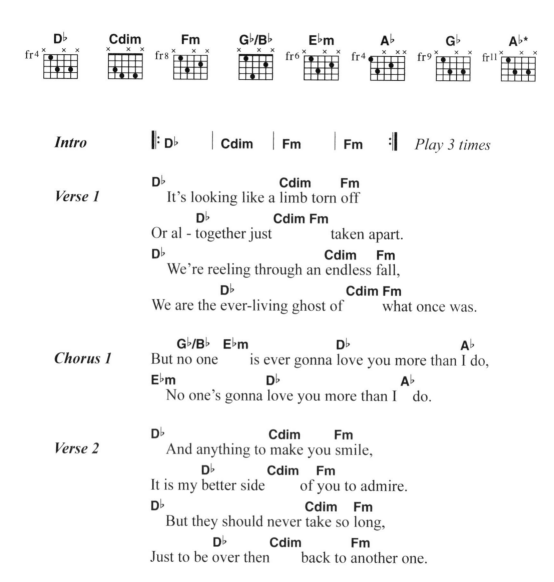

Intro   ‖: D♭ | Cdim | Fm | Fm :‖   *Play 3 times*

Verse 1

D♭   Cdim   Fm
  It's looking like a limb torn off
      D♭   Cdim Fm
Or al - together just   taken apart.
D♭   Cdim   Fm
  We're reeling through an endless fall,
        D♭   Cdim Fm
We are the ever-living ghost of   what once was.

Chorus 1

    G♭/B♭ E♭m   D♭   A♭
But no one   is ever gonna love you more than I do,
E♭m   D♭   A♭
  No one's gonna love you more than I   do.

Verse 2

D♭   Cdim   Fm
  And anything to make you smile,
     D♭   Cdim   Fm
It is my better side   of you to admire.
D♭   Cdim   Fm
  But they should never take so long,
     D♭   Cdim   Fm
Just to be over then   back to another one.

Chorus 2

     G♭/B♭ E♭m   D♭   A♭
And no one   is ever gonna love you more than I do,

E♭m   D♭   A♭
  No one's gonna love you more than I do.

Bridge 1

      Fm
But someone,

                G♭   A♭*
They could have warned you,

       D♭   Fm
When things start splitting at the seams and now

G♭   A♭*
  The whole thing's tumbling   down.

D♭   Fm   G♭ A♭*
Things start splitting at the seams and now,

      D♭   Fm
If things start splitting at the seams and now,

G♭   A♭*   D♭   Fm G♭ A♭*
  It's tumbling   down hard.

Verse 3

D♭   Cdim   Fm
  Yeah, anything to make you smile,

             D♭   Cdim Fm
You are the ever-living ghost of   what once was.

D♭   Cdim   Fm
  I never want to hear you say

               D♭   Cdim Fm
That you'd be better off   or you liked it that way.

Chorus 3

     G♭/B♭ E♭m   D♭   A♭
And no one   is ever gonna love you more than I do,

E♭m   D♭   A♭
  No one's gonna love you more than I   do.

Bridge 2

      Fm
But someone,

                G♭   A♭*
They should have warned you,

       D♭   Fm
When things start splitting at the seams and now

G♭   A♭*
  The whole thing's tumbling   down.

D♭   Fm   G♭ A♭*
Things start splitting at the seams and now,

      D♭   Fm
If things start splitting at the seams and now,

G♭   A♭*   D♭   Fm G♭ A♭* D♭
  It's tumbling   down hard.

Now That I Know

Words & Music by
Devendra Banhart

A/E   A13   A13sus4   A

fr 5   fr 4

Capo third fret

Intro ‖: A/E | A13 | A13sus4 | A :‖

Verse 1

(A)   A/E   A13
Now that I know the way it goes,

        A13sus4   A
You gotta pay back every penny that you owe.

          A/E   A13
Twelve years   old in your mama's clothes,

A13sus4   A
Shut the blinds and lock up every door.

          A/E   A13
And if you hear someone's coming near

        A13sus4   A
Just close your eyes and make 'em disap - pear now.

      A/E   A13
Mmm, mmm,

    A13sus4   A
Mmm._____

Verse 2

(A)   A/E   A13
Years a - way finds me here today,

A13sus4   A
On my own and knowledge of my way now.

          A/E   A13
So I send my friends gifts from where I've been,

A13sus4   A
Something for the hand that never there to lend.

          A/E   A13
Better keep those eyes climbing paradise

        A13sus4   A
And don't pretend you won't reach it in the end now.

      A/E   A13
Mmm, mmm,

    A13sus4   A
Mmm._____

Verse 3

(A)   A/E   A13
Dearest dear, I know you've been near,

A13sus4   A
Why'd you run, tell me why'd you disap - pear now?

               A/E A13
That you're not   here with me,

A13sus4   A
Seems to be the only time I can see you clearly.

        A/E   A13
I may not   know how to treat or give you what you need,

      A13sus4   A
But I am a gentleman who says what he means now.

    A/E A13
Mmm, mmm,

A13sus4 A
Mmm._____

Verse 4

(A)   A/E   A13
And now I sing up - on my knees,

    A13sus4   A
And praise the kindness of a gentle breeze.

      A/E   A13
I see it swell like a story in me to tell,

    A13sus4   A
Told years away and past my day of dying.

        A/E A13
So you raise them up to heaven, always hell

    A13sus4   A
There are nowhere to share or give a hand to help some.

              A/E   A13
Or you give them a - way, but they'll come back to you someday,

    A13sus4   A
Want to know why nobody was ever there to help her.

         A/E   A13
And I know it ain't fair and if God forbid you care,

    A13sus4   A
It's e - nough to get you in a whole lot of trouble.

      A/E   A13
I rea - lize it ain't wise to idealize

    A13sus4   A
Or put your life in the hands of any struggle.

cont.
A/E A¹³
Mmm, mmm,

A¹³sus⁴ A
Mmm.____

A/E A¹³
Mmm, mmm,

A¹³sus⁴ A
Mmm.____

Verse 5

(A)   A/E   A¹³
Never re - nounce or ever claim to be,

A¹³sus⁴   A
Never buy that freedom, just ain't   free now.

A/E A¹³
Ella sang sifting in the sand,

A¹³sus⁴   A
Like a hymn within to help us under - stand.

A/E   A¹³
Heaven a - waits, we're making our last stand,

A¹³sus⁴   A
Glory bound and sparrow in our   hand.

A/E A¹³
Mmm, mmm,

A¹³sus⁴ A
Mmm.____

O Valencia!

Words & Music by
Colin Meloy

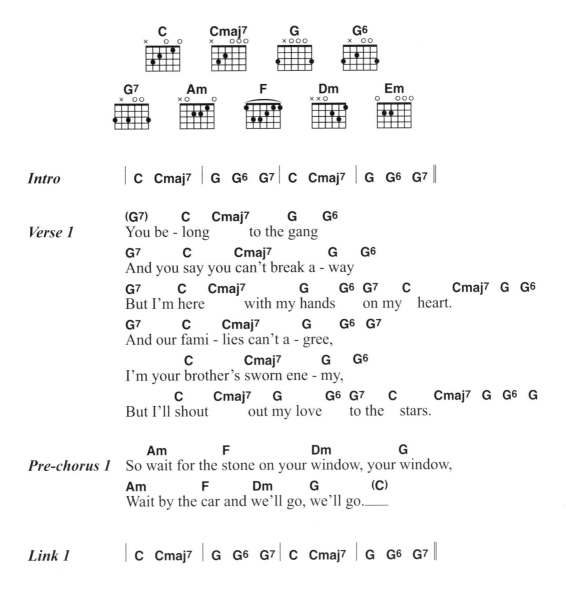

Intro   ‖: C Cmaj⁷ │ G G⁶ G⁷ │ C Cmaj⁷ │ G G⁶ G⁷ :‖

Verse 1
(G⁷)   C   Cmaj⁷   G   G⁶
You be - long   to the gang

G⁷   C   Cmaj⁷   G   G⁶
And you say you can't break a - way

G⁷   C   Cmaj⁷   G   G⁶ G⁷   C   Cmaj⁷ G G⁶
But I'm here   with my hands   on my   heart.

G⁷   C   Cmaj⁷   G   G⁶ G⁷
And our fami - lies can't a - gree,

C   Cmaj⁷   G   G⁶
I'm your brother's sworn ene - my,

C   Cmaj⁷ G   G⁶ G⁷   C   Cmaj⁷ G G⁶ G
But I'll shout   out my love   to the   stars.

Pre-chorus 1
Am   F   Dm   G
So wait for the stone on your window, your window,

Am   F   Dm   G   (C)
Wait by the car and we'll go, we'll go.___

Link 1   ‖: C Cmaj⁷ │ G G⁶ G⁷ │ C Cmaj⁷ │ G G⁶ G⁷ :‖

Verse 2

       C   Cmaj⁷   G   G⁶ G⁷
When first   we laid eyes,

    C   Cmaj⁷   G   G⁶ G
I swore to no compro - mise,

       C Cmaj⁷   G   G⁶ G⁷   C   Cmaj⁷ G G⁶
Till I felt   my ca - ress   on your   skin.

G⁷   C   Cmaj⁷   G   G⁶ G⁷
But how soon we were be - trayed,

       C   Cmaj⁷   G   G⁶
Your sister gave us a - way

G⁷   C Cmaj⁷   G G⁶ G⁷ C   Cmaj⁷ G G⁶ G
And your fa - ther came all   un - hinged.

Pre-chorus 2

       Am   F   Dm   G
So wait for the stone on your window, your window,

Am   F   Dm   G
Wait by the car and we'll go, we'll go.

Chorus 1

C   Em   Am
But oh, Va - lencia,___

          F   C
With your blood still warm on the ground.

       Em   Am
Va - lencia,___

      F   Dm   G
And I swear to the stars I'll burn this whole city down.

Link 2   ‖: C Cmaj⁷ | G G⁶ G⁷ | C Cmaj⁷ | G G⁶ G⁷ :‖

Verse 3

      C   G⁷
All I heard was a shout

         C   G⁷
Of your brother calling me out

         C   G⁷   C   G⁷
And you ran like a fool to my side.

        C   Cmaj⁷   G   G⁶
Well the shot,   it hit hard

G⁷   C   Cmaj⁷   G   G⁶
And your frame went limp in my arms,

G⁷   C   Cmaj⁷   G   G⁶ G⁷   C   Cmaj⁷ G G⁶ G
And an oath   of love was your dying cry.

Pre-chorus 3

    Am   F   Dm   G

So wait for the stone on your window, your window,

Am   F   Dm   G

Wait by the car and we'll go, we'll go.

Chorus 2

C   Em   Am

But oh, Va - lencia,___

         F   C

With your blood still warm on the ground.

    Em   Am

Va - lencia,___

         F   C

And I'll burn this whole city down.

    Em   Am

Va - lencia,___

         F   C

With your blood getting cold on the ground.

    Em   Am

Va - lencia,___

      F   Dm   G   C

And I swear to the stars I'll burn this whole city down.___

Oh No

Words & Music by
Andrew Bird

C   A   G   Dm

Fm   G7   Cmaj7   Fmaj7#11   Fmaj7

Capo third fret

Intro

C	A	C	A	
Dm	G	Dm	G	G
Dm	G	Dm	G	
Dm	G	Fm	C	

Verse 1

(C)   Dm   G7
In the salsify mains of what was thought but unsaid,
       Cmaj7   Fmaj13#11
All the calcified arhythmitists were doing the math.
     Dm   G7
And it would take a calculated blow to the head
     Cmaj7   A
To light the eyes of all the harmless sociopaths.

Chorus 1

       Dm   G
Oh, arm and arm we are the harmless sociopaths,
       C   Fmaj7
Oh, arm and arm with all the harmless sociopaths.
Dm   G
Calcium mines were buried deep in your chest.
       C   A
Oh, the calcium mines you buried deep in your chest.

Bridge 1

Dm   G   Dm   G
Ooh,   you're deep in a mine.
Dm   G   Dm   G
Ooh,   a calcium mine, oh.___

Verse 2

```
       (G)          C                        A
Well, let's get out of here past the atmosphere,
               C                            A
Squint your eyes and no one dies or goes to jail.
             C                A
Past the silver bridge, oh the silver bridge
             C                        G
Wearing nothing but a one-sie and a veil.
```

Bridge 2

```
Dm     G                 Dm      G
  Ooh,   you're deep in a mine, oh.___
Dm     G              Dm         G
  Ooh,   a calcium mine, oh no.
```

Chorus 2

```
Dm                              G
Arm and arm we are the harmless sociopaths,
     C                             Fmaj7
Oh, arm and arm with all the harmless sociopaths.
        Dm              G
In the calcium mines buried deep in your chest,
       C                A
Oh, the calcium mines buried deep in your chest.
```

Bridge 3

```
Dm     G          Dm        G
  Ooh,   deep in a mine, oh no,
Dm     G          Dm        G
  Ooh,   calcium mines, oh no.
Dm    G  Dm      G  Dm      G  Fm  C
  Ooh.___    Ooh.___    Ooh.___
```

Verse 3

```
              C                  A
So let's get out of here past the atmosphere
               C                            A
Squint your eyes and no one dies or goes to jail
             C                A
Past the silver bridge, oh the silver bridge
             C                        G
Wearing nothing but a one-sie and a veil
       C  A    C  A    C  A    C  A
Oh no,   oh no,   oh no,   oh no.
```

Outro

```
‖: C      | A      | C      | A     :‖  Play 5 times

  | C      | A        ‖
```

1234

Words & Music by
Sally Seltmann & Feist

D5   D5/C♯   Bm   G   D   Em   A

⑥ = D   ③ = G
⑤ = A   ② = B
④ = D   ① = E

Intro | D5 D5/C♯ | Bm G | D5 D5/C♯ | Bm G ||

Verse 1
D5   D5/C♯   Bm   G
One, two, three, four, tell me that you love me more.
D5   D5/C♯   Bm   G
Sleepless long nights, that is what my youth was for.
D   Em   Bm   G
Old teen - age hopes are a - live at your door,
D   Em   Bm   G
Left you with nothing but they want some more.

Chorus 1
A   G
Oh, oh, oh, you're changing your heart.
A   G
Oh, oh, oh, you know who you are.

Verse 2
D5   D5/C♯   Bm   G
Sweetheart, bitter heart, now I can tell you apart.
D5   D5/C♯   Bm   G
Cosy and cold, put the horse be - fore the cart.
D   Em   Bm   G
Those teen - age hopes who have tears in their eyes,
D   Em   Bm   G
Too scared to own up to one lit - tle lie.

Chorus 2   As Chorus 1

Bridge 1

D5   D5/C♯   Bm   G
One, two, three, four, five, six, nine or ten,

D5   D5/C♯   Bm   G   D5
Money can't buy you back the love that you had then.

| D5 D5/C♯ | Bm G | D5 D5/C♯ | Bm G |
(then.)

D5   D5/C♯   Bm   G
One, two, three, four, five, six, nine or ten,

D5   D5/C♯   Bm   G   (D5)
Money can't buy you back the love that you had then.

| D5 D5/C♯ | Bm G | D5 D5/C♯ | Bm G   ‖
(then.)

Chorus 3

A   G
Oh, oh, oh, you're changing your heart.

A   G
Oh, oh, oh, you know who you are.

A   G
Oh, oh, oh, you're changing your heart.

A   G   D Em Bm G
Oh, oh, oh, you know who you are._____

               D   Em Bm G
Who you are.____

Interlude

‖: D5 Em | Bm G | D5 Em | Bm G :‖ *Play 3 times*

Outro

D   Em Bm
For,

G   D   Em Bm G
For the teen - age boys,

                     D   Em Bm
They're breaking your heart.

G   D   Em Bm G
For the teen - age boys,

                     D   D5/C♯ Bm G
They're breaking your heart.

| D5 D5/C♯ | Bm G | D   ‖

Open Up Your Door

Words & Music by
Richard Hawley

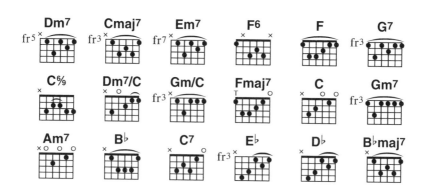

Verse 1

N.C.   **Dm7**
Open up your door,

             Cmaj7
I can't see your face no more.

          Dm7
Love is so hard to find

             Cmaj7
And even harder to de - fine.

         Dm7
Oh, open up your door,

       Em7
'Cause we've time to give

     F6   **F**   **G7**
And I'm feeling it so much more.

         Dm7 **G7**
Open up the door,

           Cmaj7 **C%** **Cmaj7**
Open up your door.

Instrumental 1 | Dm7/C | Dm7/C | Cmaj7 C% | Cmaj7 C% |

           | Dm7/C | Dm7/C | Cmaj7 C% | Cmaj7 C% |

           | Dm7 | Em7 | F6 F | G7 |

           | Dm7 | G7 | Cmaj7 C% | Cmaj7 ‖

Verse 2

(Cmaj7)   Dm7
Open up the door,

                                 Cmaj7 C% Cmaj7
I can't hear your voice no more.

                           Dm7/C
I just want to make you smile,

                         Cmaj7 C% Cmaj7
Maybe stay with you a while.

                  Dm7
Oh, open up your door,

                   Em7
'Cause we've time to give

         F6   F   G7
And my feelings aren't so ob - scure.

                   Dm7 G7
Open up the door,

                    Cmaj7 C% Cmaj7
Open up your door.

Instrumental 2 | Gm/C | Gm/C | Fmaj7 F6 | Fmaj7 |

                 | Gm/C | C | Fmaj7 F6 | Fmaj7   ‖

Verse 3

(Fmaj7)   Gm7
So open up the door,

                   Am7
'Cause we've time to give

         Bb   C7
And I'm feeling it so much more.

                   Gm7 C7
Open up your door,

                  Fmaj7 Dm7
Oh, open up your door.

                  Gm7 C7
Love is so hard to find

                  Fmaj7 Dm7
And even harder to de - fine.

                Gm7 C7
Oh, open up the door,

                  Fmaj7 Dm7
And I've never been so sure.

                Gm7 C7
Oh, open up the door,

             Fmaj7 Eb Db C7 Bbmaj7
Open up the door.

Orange Sky

Words & Music by
Alexi Murdoch

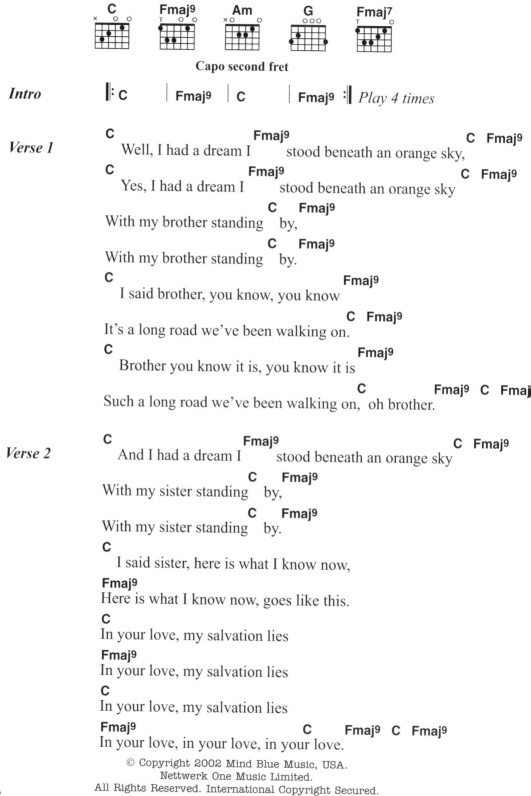

C   Fmaj9   Am   G   Fmaj7

Capo second fret

Intro   ‖: C | Fmaj9 | C | Fmaj9 :‖ *Play 4 times*

Verse 1
C   Fmaj9   C Fmaj9
   Well, I had a dream I   stood beneath an orange sky,
C   Fmaj9   C Fmaj9
   Yes, I had a dream I   stood beneath an orange sky
                    C   Fmaj9
With my brother standing   by,
                    C   Fmaj9
With my brother standing   by.
C   Fmaj9
   I said brother, you know, you know

                         C Fmaj9
It's a long road we've been walking on.
C   Fmaj9
   Brother you know it is, you know it is

                        C   Fmaj9 C Fmaj
Such a long road we've been walking on, oh brother.

Verse 2
C   Fmaj9   C Fmaj9
   And I had a dream I   stood beneath an orange sky
                 C   Fmaj9
With my sister standing   by,
                 C   Fmaj9
With my sister standing   by.
C
   I said sister, here is what I know now,
Fmaj9
Here is what I know now, goes like this.
C
In your love, my salvation lies
Fmaj9
In your love, my salvation lies
C
In your love, my salvation lies
Fmaj9   C   Fmaj9 C Fmaj9
In your love, in your love, in your love.

Bridge 1

```
      Am           G                   Fmaj7
Oh,   but sister   you know I'm so       weary,
  Am               G                 Fmaj7
   And you know si - ster my heart's been broken.
  Am              G              Fmaj7        C   Fmaj9
Sometimes, some - times my mind is too strong to carry on,
              C          Fmaj9
Too strong to carry on.
```

Verse 3

```
  C                        Fmaj9
   But when I am alone,
                                        C         Fmaj9
When I've thrown off the weight of this cra - zy stone.
                                       C
When I've lost all care for the things I own,
                                     Fmaj9
That's when I miss you, that's when I miss you,
                                   C   Fmaj9
That's when I miss you, you who are my home,
                      C   Fmaj9
You who are my home.
  C
   And here is what I know now,
           Fmaj9
Here is what I      know now, goes like this.
     C
‖: In your love, my salvation lies,
Fmaj9
In your love, my salvation lies. :‖ Play 3 times
C
In your love, my salvation lies
Fmaj9                            C        Fmaj9  C  Fmaj9  C  Fmaj9
   In your love, in your love, in your love.
```

Verse 4

```
  C                      Fmaj9                       C   Fmaj9
   Well, I had a dream I      stood beneath an orange sky,
  C                    Fmaj9                      C   Fmaj9
   Yes, I had a dream I      stood beneath an orange sky
                           C          Fmaj9
With my brother and my sister standing by,
                         C          Fmaj9
With my brother and my sister   standing by,
  C                          C
With my brother and my sister   standing by.
```

Postcards From Italy

Words & Music by
Zachary Condon

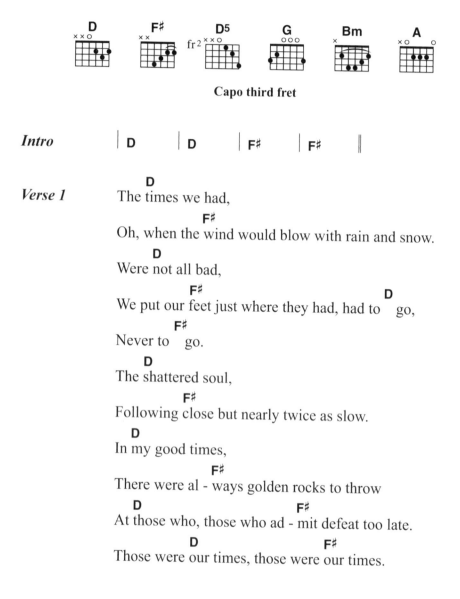

Capo third fret

Intro | D | D | F♯ | F♯ ‖

Verse 1

        D
The times we had,

          F♯
Oh, when the wind would blow with rain and snow.

      D
Were not all bad,

          F♯   **D**
We put our feet just where they had, had to go,

        F♯
Never to go.

      D
The shattered soul,

        F♯
Following close but nearly twice as slow.

    D
In my good times,

         F♯
There were al - ways golden rocks to throw

    D   **F♯**
At those who, those who ad - mit defeat too late.

           D   **F♯**
Those were our times, those were our times.

Instrumental ‖: D | D | F♯ | F♯ :‖ *Play 5 times*

| D | D | D5 | D5 ‖

‖: G | D | Bm | A :‖

Bridge

       G   D   Bm   A
And I will love to see that day, that day is mine,
          G   D   Bm   A
When she will marry me out - side with the willow trees.
       G   D   Bm   A
And play___ the songs we made, they made me so,
       G   D   Bm   A
And I would love to see that day, her day was mine.

Outro ‖: G | D | Bm | A :‖ *Play 10 times to fade*

151

Proof

Words & Music by
John Bramwell, Andrew Hargreaves & Peter Jobson

C(add9)   Bm(add11)   Am11   G   C/G

6 = E   3 = G   **Capo fourth fret**
5 = A   2 = B
4 = D   1 = D

Intro
‖: C(add9) | Bm(add11) | Am11 | G   C/G :‖

Verse 1

    C(add9)   Bm(add11)
And hey, could you stand another   drink?
               Am11
I'm better when I don't think,
               G   C/G
It seems to get me through.
    C(add9)   Bm(add11)
And say, d'you wanna spin another   line?
           Am11
Like we had a good time,
              G   C/G
Not that I need proof.

Verse 2

C(add9)   Bm(add11)
Swell, we're living in a ho - tel,
             Am11
Someone's ringing my   bell
               G   C/G
In a room without a view.
    C(add9)   Bm(add11)
And hey, heard you read another   book
            Am11
Should I take another look,
         C(add9) Bm(add11)
Who am I without you?
   Am11 G C/G
Ah hoo, ah,
   C(add9) Bm(add11)
Ah hoo,   ah,
Am11 G C/G
Ah.

Verse 3	As Verse 1
Verse 4	As Verse 2

Outro

C(add9)
La la la la la la la la la la,

Bm(add11)
La la la la la la.

Am11
La la la la la la la la la,

G   **C/G**
La la la la la la.

C(add9)
La la la la la la la la la,

Bm(add11)
La la la la la la.

Am11
La la la la la la la la la,

                      G
La la la la la la la la la la.

Bon Iver

Re: Stacks

Words & Music by
Justin Vernon

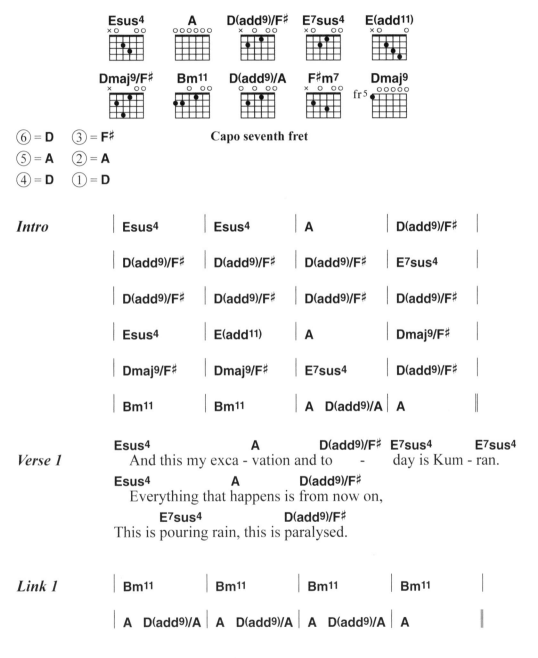

$\textcircled{6}$ = D $\textcircled{3}$ = F♯

$\textcircled{5}$ = A $\textcircled{2}$ = A

$\textcircled{4}$ = D $\textcircled{1}$ = D

Capo seventh fret

Intro

| Esus⁴ | Esus⁴ | A | D(add⁹)/F♯ |

| D(add⁹)/F♯ | D(add⁹)/F♯ | D(add⁹)/F♯ | E⁷sus⁴ |

| D(add⁹)/F♯ | D(add⁹)/F♯ | D(add⁹)/F♯ | D(add⁹)/F♯ |

| Esus⁴ | E(add¹¹) | A | Dmaj⁹/F♯ |

| Dmaj⁹/F♯ | Dmaj⁹/F♯ | E⁷sus⁴ | D(add⁹)/F♯ |

| Bm¹¹ | Bm¹¹ | A D(add⁹)/A | A ‖

Verse 1

Esus⁴   A   D(add⁹)/F♯   E⁷sus⁴   E⁷sus⁴
And this my exca - vation and to   -   day is Kum - ran.

Esus⁴   A   D(add⁹)/F♯
Everything that happens is from now on,

     E⁷sus⁴   D(add⁹)/F♯
This is pouring rain, this is paralysed.

Link 1

| Bm¹¹ | Bm¹¹ | Bm¹¹ | Bm¹¹ |

| A D(add⁹)/A | A D(add⁹)/A | A D(add⁹)/A | A ‖

Verse 2

| Esus⁴ | A | D(add9)/F♯ | E⁷sus⁴ | D(add9)F♯ |

Esus^4　　　　　　　　A　　　D(add^9)/F♯　E^{7}sus^4　　　　　D(add^9)F♯
　I keep throwing it down two　　　　hundred at a time.

Esus^4　　　　　　　A　　　　D(add^9)/F♯
　It's hard to find it when you knew it,

　　　　　　　　　　E^{7}sus^4　　　　　D(add^9)/F♯
When your money's gone and you're drunk as hell.

Link 2

| Bm¹¹ | Bm¹¹ | Bm¹¹ | Bm¹¹ | |

‖ A　D(add^9)/A | A　D(add^9)/A | A　D(add^9)/A | A ‖

Chorus 1

A　　　Esus^4　　　　　　　F♯m^7　　　Dmaj^9
On your back with your racks as the stacks you load,

　　　Esus^4　　　　　　　F♯m^7　　　　Dmaj^9
In the back with your racks and the stacks are your load,

　　　Esus^4　　　　　　　　　　F♯m^7　　　Dmaj^9
In the back with your racks and you're un - stacking your load.

Verse 3

Esus^4　　　　　　　　　　A　D(add^9)/F♯　E^{7}sus^4　　　　D(add^9)F♯
　And I've been twisting to the sun_____I needed to re - place.

Esus^4　　　　　　　　A　　　D(add^9)/F♯
　And the fountain in the front yard is rusted out,

　　　　　　E^{7}sus^4　　D(add^9)/F♯
All my love was down in a frozen ground.

Link 3

| Bm¹¹ | Bm¹¹ | Bm¹¹ | Bm¹¹ | |

‖ A　D(add^9)/A | A　D(add^9)/A | A　D(add^9)/A | A ‖

Verse 4

Esus^4　　　　　　　　A　　　D(add^9)/F♯
　There's a black crow sitting a - cross from me;

　　E^{7}sus^4　　　D(add^9)F♯
His wiry legs are crossed.

Esus^4　　　　　　　　A　　　　D(add^9)/F♯
　And he's dangling my keys, he even fakes a toss,

　　　　　　E^{7}sus^4　　D(add^9)/F♯　Bm¹¹
Whatever could it be that has brought me to___ this loss?

Link 4 ‖ A D(add9)/A ‖ A D(add9)/A ‖ A D(add9)/A ‖ A   ‖

Chorus 2 As Chorus 1

Verse 5

Esus⁴   A   D(add9)/F♯ E⁷sus⁴   D(add9)/F♯
  This is not the sound of a new man or crispy reali - sation.

Esus⁴   A   D(add9)/F♯
  It's the sound of the un - locking and the lift away,

                        E⁷sus⁴ D(add9)/F♯
Your love will be   safe with me.

Outro ‖ Bm¹¹   ‖ Bm¹¹   ‖ Bm¹¹   ‖ Bm¹¹   ‖

‖ A D(add9)/A ‖ A D(add9)/A ‖ A D(add9)/A ‖ A   ‖

157

Rinse Me Down

Words & Music by
Jack Steadman

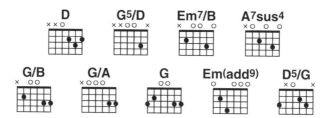

Capo second fret

Intro ‖: D | D | G5/D :‖ *Play 3 times*

| D | D | D |

| Em7/B | Em7/B | A7sus4 | A7sus4 |

| G/B | G/A | G | G |

| G/B | G/A | G | G |

| G | G | Em(add9) | Em(add9) |

| Em(add9) | Em(add9) | D5/G | D5/G |

| D5/G | D5/G | Em(add9) | Em(add9) | Em(add9) | Em(add9) |

‖: D | D | G5/D :‖ *Play 3 times*

| D | D | D |

Verse 1

Em⁷/B   A⁷sus⁴ G/B   G/A   G   G/B   G/A   G

Chasing the night to make it   right,_____

               Em(add⁹)   D⁵/G

Oh, and you had it,_____

               Em(add⁹)

Caught like a rabbit.

Link 1

‖: D | D | G⁵/D :‖ *Play 3 times*

| D | D | D   ‖

Verse 2

Em⁷/B   A⁷sus⁴   G/B   G/A   G   G/B   G/A   G

Told you to wait, but it's   too   late,_____

               Em(add⁹)   D⁵/G

You got your man,_____

               Em(add⁹)

Rinsing him down.

Link 2

‖: D | D | G⁵/D :‖ *Play 3 times*

| D | D | D   ‖

Instrumental

| Em⁷/B | Em⁷/B | A⁷sus⁴ | A⁷sus⁴ |

| G/B | G/A | G | G |

| G/B | G/A | G | G |

| G | G | Em(add⁹) | Em(add⁹) |

| Em(add⁹) | Em(add⁹) | D⁵/G | D⁵/G |

| D⁵/G | D⁵/G | Em(add⁹) | Em(add⁹) | Em(add⁹) | Em(add⁹) |

‖: D | D | G⁵/D :‖ *Play 3 times*

| D | D | D   ‖

Verse 3

Em7/B   A7sus4 G/B G/A G   G/B G/A G
Turning your head to mine in - stead,_____

              Em(add9) D5/G
Gave me the eyes,_____

              Em(add9)
Burning like light.

Link 3

‖: D		D		G5/D	:‖	*Play 3 times*
D		D		D	‖	

Outro

Em7/B	Em7/B	A7sus4	A7sus4
G/B	G/A	G	G
G/B	G/A	G	G
G	G	Em(add9)	Em(add9)
Em(add9)	Em(add9)	D5/G	D5/G
D5/G	D5/G	Em(add9)	Em(add9)
Em(add9)	Em(add9)	D ‖	

160

Roscoe

Words & Music by
Tim Smith

Intro | G♯m | G♯m | G♯m | G♯m   ‖

Verse 1
G♯m
Stonecutters made them from
F♯   E
Stones chosen specially for   you and I,
                    G♯m
Who will live inside.

The mountaineers gathered tender,
F♯   E
Piled high, in which to take a - long,
                                              G♯m
Driving many miles, knowing they'd get here.

When they got here, all exhausted,
          F♯
On the roof leaks they got started.
          E   G♯
And now when the rain comes, we can be thankful.

Chorus 1
G♯   F♯   E
Ooh, ah, ooh, when the mountain - eers
                                                          G♯m
Saw that everything fit, they were glad and so they took off.
                              F♯   E   G♯m
Thought we were de - void, a change or two around this place.
              F♯   E   G♯m
When they get back they're all mixed up with no one to stay with.

Link 1 | G♯m | G♯m | F♯ |

         | F♯ | E | E   ‖

(The village)

Verse 2

               G♯m
The village used to be all one really needs,

               F♯
Now it's filled with hundreds and hundreds of chemicals,

             E
That mostly sur - round you.

                                       G♯m
You wish to flee, but it's not like you, so listen to me, listen to me.

Oh, oh, and when the morning comes, we will step outside,

              F♯
We will not find another man inside.

                      E
We like the newness, the new - ness of all

                          G♯m
That has grown in our garden soaking for so   long.

Whenever I was a child I wondered what if my name had changed

      F♯
Into something more productive like Roscoe,

            E   G♯m
Been born in eighteen ninety-one, waiting with my Aunt Rosaline.

Chorus 2

G♯m   F♯
Thought we were de - void,

            E   G♯m
A change or two around this place.

         F♯   E   G♯m
When they get back they're all mixed up with no one to stay with.

Interlude | G♯m | G♯m | F♯ | F♯ | E | E |

               | G♯m | G♯m | G♯m | G♯m | F♯ | E | E   ‖

Verse 3

E   G#m
Eighteen ninety-one,

        F#
They roamed around in the forests.

        E
They made their house from cedars,

        G#m
They made their house from stones.

     F#
Oh, they're a little like you,

       E
And they're a little like me,

   G#m
We are falling leaves.

Chorus 3

G#m   F#
Thought we were de - void,

    E   G#m
A change or two around this place,

 F#   E G#m
This place, this place.____

G#m   F#   E
When they get back they're all mixed up

       G#m
With no one to stay with.

     F#   E
When they get back they're all mixed up

       G#m
With no one to stay with.

Rock Bottom Riser

Words & Music by
Bill Callahan

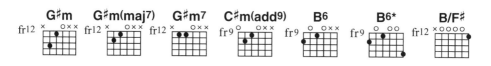

⑥ = C♯	③ = D♯
⑤ = F♯	② = F♯
④ = B	① = B

Intro | G♯m | G♯m(maj7) | G♯m7 | C♯m(add9) ‖

Verse 1

G♯m   G♯m(maj7)
  I love my mother,   I love my father,

G♯m7   C♯m(add9)
  I love my sisters too.

G♯m   G♯m(maj7)
  I bought this guitar   to pledge my love,

G♯m7   C♯m(add9)
  To pledge my love   to you.

Chorus 1

    G♯m   G♯m(maj7)
I am a rock bottom riser

G♯m7   C♯m(add9)
  And I owe it all to you.

    G♯m   G♯m(maj7)
I am a rock bottom riser

G♯m7   C♯m(add9)
  And I owe it all to you.

Bridge

B6   C♯m(add9)
I saw a gold ring at the bottom of the river

B6   C♯m(add9)
Glinting at my foolish heart.

    B6   C♯m(add9)
Oh, my foolish heart had to go diving,

B6   C♯m(add9)
Diving, diving, diving into the murk.

     B6   C♯m(add9)
And from the bottom of the river I looked up for the sun

    B6   C♯m(add9)
Which had shattered in the water, and the pieces were raining down

   B6   C♯m(add9)
Like gold rings that passed through my hands.

   B6   C♯m(add9)
As I thrashed and I grabbed, I started rising, rising, rising.

Verse 2

G♯m   G♯m(maj7)
 I left my mother,   I left my father,

G♯m7   C♯m(add9)
 I left my sisters too.

G♯m   G♯m(maj7)
 I left them standing on the banks

    G♯m7   C♯m(add9)
And they pulled me out of this mighty, mighty, mighty river.

Chorus 2   As Chorus 1

Verse 3

G♯m   G♯m(maj7)
 I love my mother,   I love my father,

G♯m7   C♯m(add9)
 I love my sisters too.

G♯m   G♯m(maj7)
 I bought this guitar to pledge my love,

G♯m7   C♯m(add9) B6* B/F♯
 To pledge my love to you

Rosyln

Words & Music by
Justin Vernon

Fmaj7   G6   C   D7sus2   G6/D   Am7   C/E

Capo first fret

Intro

| Fmaj7 | Fmaj7 | Fmaj7 | G6 |

| Fmaj7 | Fmaj7 | Fmaj7 | Fmaj7 |

| C | D7sus2 | D7sus2 | D7sus2 | D7sus2 |

| C | D7sus2 | D7sus2 | D7sus2 | G6 Fmaj7 G6/D ‖

Verse 1

Fmaj7   (C)
Up with your turret, aren't we just terri - fied?

‖: C | D7sus2 | D7sus2 | D7sus2 :‖ G6 Fmaj7 G6/D |

Fmaj7   (C)
Shale, screen your worry from what you won't ever find.

| C | D7sus2 | D7sus2 | D7sus2 | D7sus2 |

| Am7 | D7sus2 | D7sus2 | D7sus2 | G6 Fmaj7 G6/D ‖

Chorus 1

C/E   Fmaj7
Don't let it fool you, don't let it fool you, down,

                          C   G6
Down's sitting round, folds in the gown.

Link　　　| Am⁷　　| Am⁷　　| Am⁷　　| C　　　　|

　　　　　| Am⁷　| C　　　| Am⁷　　| Am⁷　‖

Verse 2

Fmaj⁷　　　　　　　　　　　　　　　　　　(C)
　　Sea and the rock below cocked to the under - tow.

　　| C　　　| D⁷sus²　| D⁷sus²　| D⁷sus²　| D⁷sus²　|

　　| Am⁷　　| D⁷sus²　| D⁷sus²　| D⁷sus²　| G⁶ Fmaj⁷ G⁶/D |
Fmaj⁷　　　　　　　　　　　　　　　　　　　(C)
　　Bones, blood and teeth erode with every crashing node.

　　| C　　　| D⁷sus²　| D⁷sus²　| D⁷sus²　| G⁶ Fmaj⁷ G⁶/D |

　　| C　　　| D⁷sus²　| D⁷sus²　| D⁷sus²　| D⁷sus²　G⁶　| D⁷sus² G⁶ ‖

Chorus 2

C/E　　　　　　　　　　　　　　　　　　Fmaj⁷
Wings wouldn't help you, wings wouldn't help you down,
　　　　　　　　　　　C　　　　　　G⁶
Down fills the ground, gravi - ty's proud.

Instrumental　| Am⁷　　| Am⁷　　| Am⁷　　| Am⁷　　|

　　　　　　　| Fmaj⁷　| Fmaj⁷　| Fmaj⁷　| Fmaj⁷　|

　　　　　　　| Am⁷　　| Am⁷　　| Am⁷　　| Am⁷　　|

　　　　　　　| Fmaj⁷　| Fmaj⁷　| Fmaj⁷　| Fmaj⁷　|

　　　　　　　| Am⁷　　| Am⁷　　| Am⁷　　| Am⁷　‖

Verse 3

Fmaj⁷   **(C)**
You barely are blinking, wagging your face a - round.

| C | D⁷sus² | D⁷sus² | D⁷sus² | G⁶ Fmaj⁷ G⁶/D |

| C | D⁷sus² | D⁷sus² | D⁷sus² | D⁷sus²   G⁶ ‖

Fmaj⁷   **(C)**
When did this just become a mortal home? No.

| C | D⁷sus² | D⁷sus² | G⁶ Fmaj⁷ G⁶/D |

| C | D⁷sus² | D⁷sus² | D⁷sus² | D⁷sus² ‖

Fmaj⁷   **G⁶**
Won't, won't, won't, won't, won't let you talk me,
                          Fmaj⁷
Won't let you talk me down.
              C   **G⁶**
Will pull it taut, nothing let out.

Outro | Am⁷ | Am⁷ | Am⁷ | Am⁷ | Fmaj⁷ ‖

Skinny Love

Words & Music by
Justin Vernon

Am fr5 **C**   **C***   **D13(no3)** fr7   **C(add9/E)** fr7   **G(add11)/B**   **F/A**

Tune guitar slightly flat

⑥ = C   ③ = G
⑤ = G   ② = C
④ = E   ① = C

Intro

‖: Am | C | C* | C* :‖ *Play 3 times*

| D13(no3) | D13(no3) | Am | Am   C |

| C* | C* | C* | C* ‖

Verse 1

Am   C   C*
Come on skinny love just last the year,
Am   C   C*
Pour a little salt we were never here.
    Am   C   C*
My, my, my, my, my, my, my, my,
      D13(no3)   Am
Staring at the sink of blood and crushed veneer.

Link 1

| C | C | C | C ‖

Verse 2

Am   C   C*
 I tell my love to wreck it all,
Am   C   C*
Cut out all the ropes and let me fall.
    Am   C   C*
My, my, my, my, my, my, my, my,
      D13(no3)   Am
Right in this moment this order's tall.

Chorus 1

C(add9)/E
And I told you to be patient,

G(add11)/B   F/A
And I told you to be fine.

C(add9)/E
And I told you to be balanced,

G(add11)/B   F/A
And I told you to be kind.

C(add9)/E
And in the morning I'll be with you,

G(add11)/B   F/A
But it will be a different kind.

C(add9)/E
And I'll be holding all the tickets,

G(add11)/B   F/A
And you'll be owning all the fines.

Verse 3

Am   C   C*
Come on skinny love what happened here?

Am   C   C*
Suckle on the hope in light bras - sieres,

Am   C   C*
My, my, my, my, my, my, my, my,

D13(no3)   Am   F/A
Sullen load is full; so slow on the split.

Chorus 2

C(add9)/E
And I told you to be patient,

G(add11)/B   F/A
And I told you to be fine.

C(add9)/E
And I told you to be balanced,

G(add11)/B   F/A
And I told you to be kind.

C(add9)/E
And now all your love is wasted,

G(add11)/B   F/A
And then who the hell was I?

C(add9)/E
And I'm breaking at the britches,

G(add11)/B   F/A
And at the end of all your lines.

Bridge

C(add9)/E
 Who will love you?

G(add11)/B F/A
 Who will fight?

C(add9)/E   G(add11)/B   F/A
 Who will fall_____ far be - hind?

Outro

‖: Am | C | C* | C* :‖ *Play 3 times*

| D13(no3) | D13(no3) | Am | Am C | C   ‖

Say Please

Words & Music by
Conor Oberst

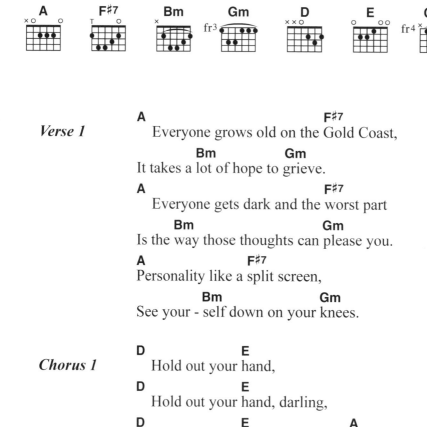

Verse 1

       A   **F♯7**
Everyone grows old on the Gold Coast,
       Bm   **Gm**
It takes a lot of hope to grieve.
   A   **F♯7**
Everyone gets dark and the worst part
     Bm   **Gm**
Is the way those thoughts can please you.
A   **F♯7**
Personality like a split screen,
     Bm   **Gm**
See your - self down on your knees.

Chorus 1

   D   **E**
Hold out your hand,
   D   **E**
Hold out your hand, darling,
   D   **E**   **A**
Hold out your hand, say please.

Guitar solo

‖: A | A | F♯7 | F♯7 |

| Bm | Bm | Gm | Gm :‖

Verse 2

A   F#7
Everyone gives up, down on hard luck,

Bm   Gm
On hope ain't enough it seems.

A   F#7
Everyone gets lost in their own fog,

Bm   Gm
Have to wander on with lantern dreams.

Bridge

C#m   Bm
Say please, please, just say something

C#m   Bm   E   D
Speak up, please if it's what you're look - ing for.

Chorus 2

D   E
Hold out your hand,

D   E
Hold out your hand, darling,

D   E   A   A♭
Hold out your hand, say please.

D   E
Hold out your hand,

D   E
Hold out your hand, darling,

D   E   A
Hold out your hand, say please.

Southern Point

Words & Music by
Daniel Rossen, Christopher Bear, Edward Droste & Christopher Taylor

Em⁷   F⁶⁄₉(♭5)   F6   B♭6   Dmaj⁹

Am⁷   B   Fmaj7/E   E7   D6   Dm

⑥ = D   ③ = F#
⑤ = A   ② = B
④ = D   ① = D

Intro   ‖: Em⁷ | Em⁷ | F⁶⁄₉(♭5) | F⁶⁄₉(♭5) :‖

Verse 1
> **Em⁷**   **F⁶⁄₉(♭5)**
> Our haven on the southern point is calling us.
> **Em⁷**   **F⁶⁄₉(♭5)**
> Our haven on the southern point is calling us.
> **Em⁷**   **F⁶⁄₉(♭5)**
> And faced with all the obvious, so carry us.
> **Em⁷**   **F⁶⁄₉(♭5)**
> A - vert your eyes from all of this, we'll make it all back.

Link 1 | F6 | B♭6 | Dmaj⁹ | Am⁷ ‖

Chorus 1
> **Am⁷   Dmaj⁹   Am⁷**
>   In the end
> **Dmaj⁹   Am⁷**
> You'll never find,
> **Dmaj⁹   Am⁷**
> You'll never find.
> **Dmaj⁹   Am⁷**
> In the end, (You'll never find me now.)
> **Dmaj⁹   Am⁷**
> In the end, (You'll never find me now.)
> **Dmaj⁹   Am⁷**
> You'll never find, (But I'll re - turn to you.)
> **Dmaj⁹   Am⁷**
> You'll never find. (When you re - turn to me.)

Link 2

| Dmaj⁹ | Dmaj⁹ | Am⁷ | |

| Dmaj⁹ | Dmaj⁹ | Am⁷ | |

| F6 | B♭6 | Dmaj⁹ | Am⁷ ‖

In the end.

Chorus 2   As Chorus 1

Link 3

| Dmaj⁹ | Dmaj⁹ | Am⁷ | |

| Dmaj⁹ | Dmaj⁹ | Am⁷ | F6 | B♭6 ‖

Bridge 1

B   Fmaj⁷/E E⁷
In regards to the last   word,

           Fmaj⁷/E B
It's not the last you'll hear.

                  Fmaj⁷/E E⁷
I never find any other,

           Fmaj⁷/E E⁷
I could ever,

           Fmaj⁷/E D6
I could ever.

Link 4

| Dmaj⁹ | Dmaj⁹ | Am⁷ | |

| Dmaj⁹ | Dmaj⁹ | Am⁷ | F6 | B♭6 ‖

Bridge 2

B   Fmaj⁷/E E⁷
Never say it's the last   word,

           Fmaj⁷/E B
It's not the last   word.

           Fmaj⁷/E E⁷
I never find any other,

           Fmaj⁷/E E⁷
I could ever,

           Fmaj⁷/E D6
I could ever.

Outro

| Dmaj⁹ | Am⁷ | Dmaj⁹ | Am⁷ | |

| Dm | Am⁷ | Dm | Am⁷ | Dmaj⁹ ‖

Start Wearing Purple

Words & Music by
Eugene Hütz, Sergey Ryabtsev, Eliot Ferguson,
Oren Kaplan, Yuri Lemeshev & Rea Mochiach

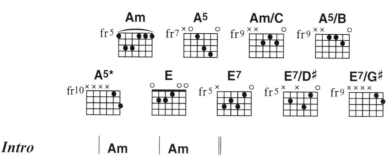

Intro | Am | Am ‖

Chorus 1
A5   Am/C   A5/B   A5*   A5   Am/C A5/B A5*
Start wearing purple, wearing purple,

A5   Am/C   A5*   Am/C   E
Start wearing purple for me now.

          E7   E7/D♯   E7/G♯   E7   E7/D♯
All your sanity   and wits they will all vanish,

          E7/G♯   E   Am
I promise,   it's   just a matter of time.

N.C.
So yeah, ha.

Chorus 2
Am
Start wearing purple, wearing purple,

                              E
Start wearing purple for me now.

All your sanity and wits they will all vanish

                              Am
I promise, it's just a matter of time.

Verse 1
N.C.   Am
I've known you since you were a twenty, and I was twenty,

                              E
And thought that some years from now

A purple little little lady will be perfect

                              Am
For dirty old and useless clown.

N.C.
So yeah, ha.

Chorus 3

Am
Start wearing purple, wearing purple,

                                          E
Start wearing purple for me now.

All your sanity and wits they will all vanish,

                                    Am
I promise, it's just a matter of time.

Verse 2

N.C.   Am
I know it all from Dio - genis to Foucault

                          E⁷
From Lozgechkin to Paspar - tu

I ja kljanus obostzav dva paltza

                             Am N.C.
Schto muziko poshla ot Zzukov Mu!

Chorus 4

Am
Start wearing purple, wearing purple,

                                          E
Start wearing purple for me now.

All your sanity and wits they will all vanish,

                                    Am
I promise, it's just a matter of time.
N.C.
So yeah, huh, ha, ha.

Chorus 5

Am
Start wearing purple, wearing purple,

                                        E
Start wearing purple for me now.

Link 1
(free time)

E
So why don't you start wearing purple,

Why don't you start wearing purple.
N.C.
Start wearing purple for me now!

Chorus 6 | Am | Am | Am | E   ‖

E
All your sanity and wits, they will all vanish,

                                    Am
I promise, it's just a matter of time.

                 N.C.   Am   E
Link 2   So Fio-Fio-Fio - letta! Etta! Va-va-va-vaja dama ti mo - ja!

                                                                    Am
                 Eh podayte nam karetu, votetu, i mi poedem k eben - jam!
                 N.C.
                 So yeah, ah.

                 Am
Chorus 7   Start wearing purple, wearing purple,

                                           E
                 Start wearing purple for me now.

                 All your sanity and wits, they will all vanish,

                                           Am
                 I promise, it's just a matter of time.

Fleet Foxes

Tiger Mountain Peasant Song

Words & Music by
Robin Pecknold

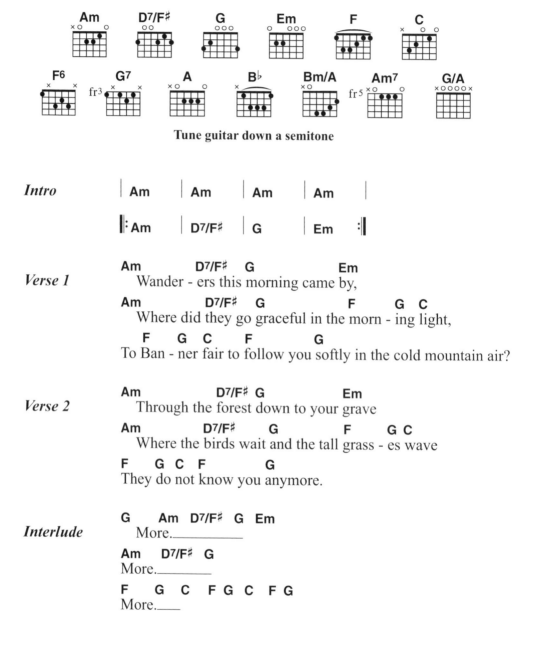

Tune guitar down a semitone

Intro

| Am | Am | Am | Am | |

‖: Am | D7/F♯ | G | Em :‖

Verse 1

Am   D7/F♯ G   Em
Wander - ers this morning came by,

Am   D7/F♯ G   F   G C
Where did they go graceful in the morn - ing light,

     F   G   C   F   G
To Ban - ner fair to follow you softly in the cold mountain air?

Verse 2

Am   D7/F♯ G   Em
Through the forest down to your grave

Am   D7/F♯   G   F   G C
Where the birds wait and the tall grass - es wave

F   G C F   G
They do not know you anymore.

Interlude

G   Am D7/F♯ G Em
More._____

Am   D7/F♯ G
More._____

F   G   C   F G C   F G
More.____

Chorus 1

```
C    F6        G7       C
Dear shadow a - live and well,
           F6    C
How can the body die?
     C     D7/F♯              G
You tell me everything, anything true.
```

Verse 3

```
Am        D7/F♯    G          Em
  In the town one morning I went,
Am            D7/F♯     G            F G  C
  Stagger - ing through premonitions of my death,
F G    C  F    G
I  don't see any - body that dear to me.
```

Chorus 2   As Chorus 1

Bridge

```
Em  A  C                B♭    C
Jes - se, I don't know what I have done,
    B♭          C      B♭    C
I'm turning my - self to a demon.
               B♭    C
I don't know what I have done,
    B♭          C      B♭    C
I'm turning my - self to a demon.
```

Outro

```
  Am      Bm/A  Am7  Bm/A  Am  G/A
‖: La la la la la la la la la la la    la    la la. :‖  Repeat ad lib. to fade
```

That Look You Give That Guy

Words & Music by
E & Koool G Murder

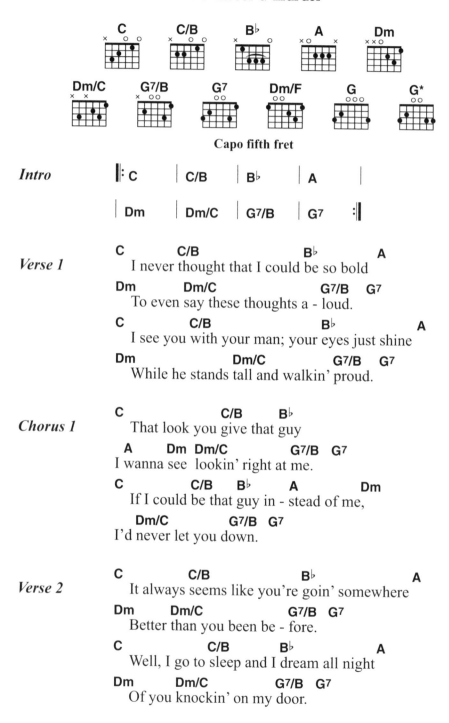

Capo fifth fret

Intro
|: C | C/B | B♭ | A |

| Dm | Dm/C | G7/B | G7 :|

Verse 1

C   C/B   B♭   A
I never thought that I could be so bold

Dm   Dm/C   G7/B   G7
To even say these thoughts a - loud.

C   C/B   B♭   A
I see you with your man; your eyes just shine

Dm   Dm/C   G7/B   G7
While he stands tall and walkin' proud.

Chorus 1

C   C/B   B♭
That look you give that guy

A   Dm Dm/C   G7/B   G7
I wanna see   lookin' right at me.

C   C/B   B♭   A   Dm
If I could be that guy in - stead of me,

Dm/C   G7/B   G7
I'd never let you down.

Verse 2

C   C/B   B♭   A
It always seems like you're goin' somewhere

Dm   Dm/C   G7/B   G7
Better than you been be - fore.

C   C/B   B♭   A
Well, I go to sleep and I dream all night

Dm   Dm/C   G7/B   G7
Of you knockin' on my door.

Chorus 2

    C   C/B   B♭
    That look you give that guy

   A   Dm Dm/C   G7/B G7
I wanna see lookin' right at me.

   C   C/B   B♭   A   Dm
   If I could be that guy in - stead of me,

   Dm/C   G7/B   G7   (C)
I'd be all I can be,   I'd be all I can be.

Instrumental 1 | C | C/B | B♭ | A |

                | Dm | Dm/F | G | G* |

                | C | C/B | B♭ | A |

                | Dm | Dm/C | G7/B | G   ‖

Verse 3

    C   C/B   B♭   A
   I'm nothin' like what I'd like to be,

Dm   Dm/C   G7/B G
   I'm nothin' much, I know it's true.

C   C/B   B♭   A
   I lack the style and the pedigree

Dm   Dm/C   G7/B G7
   And my chances are so few.

Chorus 3

    C   C/B   B♭
   That look you give that guy

   A   Dm Dm/C   G7/B G7
I wanna see lookin' right at me.

   C   C/B   B♭   A   Dm
   If I could be that guy in - stead of me,

   Dm/C   G7/B G7
I'd give you all I got.

Verse 4

```
    C         C/B               B♭        A
    I never thought that I could be so bold
    Dm        Dm/C                  G7/B  G7
    To even say these thoughts a - loud.
    C              C/B    B♭             A
    But if, let's say, it won't work out,
    Dm            Dm/C           G7/B   G7
    You know where I can be found.
```

Chorus 4

```
    C                  C/B    B♭
    That look you give that guy
      A      Dm  Dm/C         G7/B   G7
    I wanna see  lookin' right at me.
    C          C/B    B♭    A        Dm
    If I could be that guy in - stead of me,
       Dm/C         G7/B       G7          (C)
    I'd never let you down, I'd never let you down.
```

Instrumental 2

C		C/B	B♭	A	
	Dm	Dm/F	G	G*	
‖: C		C/B	B♭	A	
	Dm	Dm/C	G7/B	G*	:‖ *Repeat to fade*

184

The Underdog

Words & Music by
Britt Daniel

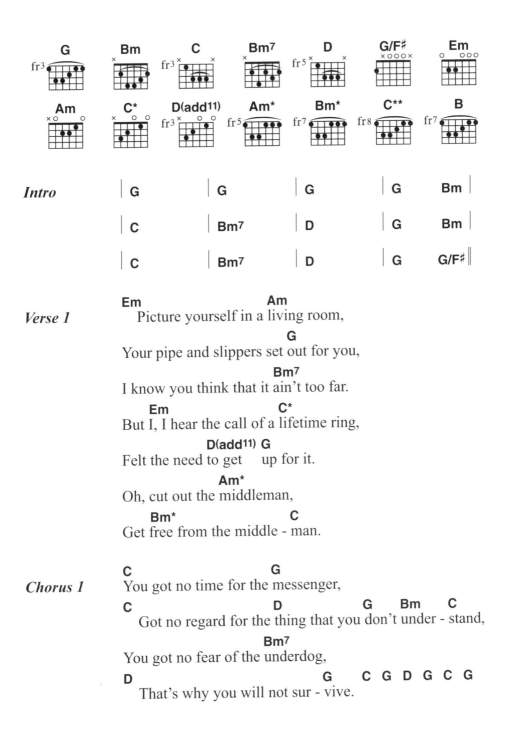

Intro

| G | | G | | G | | G | Bm |
| C | | Bm7 | | D | | G | Bm |
| C | | Bm7 | | D | | G | G/F♯ ‖

Verse 1

  Em   Am
Picture yourself in a living room,
                  G
Your pipe and slippers set out for you,
               Bm7
I know you think that it ain't too far.
   Em   C*
But I, I hear the call of a lifetime ring,
        D(add11) G
Felt the need to get   up for it.
        Am*
Oh, cut out the middleman,
   Bm*   C
Get free from the middle - man.

Chorus 1

C   G
You got no time for the messenger,
C   D   G   Bm   C
   Got no regard for the thing that you don't under - stand,
                  Bm7
You got no fear of the underdog,
D   G   C G D G C G
   That's why you will not sur - vive.

Link 1 | C | Bm7 | D | G   Bm |
           | C | Bm7 | D | G   G/F♯‖

Verse 2

Em   C
  I want to forget how con - viction fits,
                        G
But can I get out from under it?
           Bm*   C**
Can I gut it out of me? Oh, oh, oh, oh.
           G
It can't all be wedding cake,
           Am*
It can't all be boiled away,
           Bm*
I try but I can't let go of it,
B   C
Can't let go of it, na - ha.

Chorus 2

C   G
  'Cause you don't talk to the water boy,
C   D   G   Bm   C
  And there's so much you could learn but you don't want to know.
                      Bm7
You will not back up an inch ever,
D   G   C G D G C G
  That's why you will not sur - vive.

Link 2 | C | Bm7 | D | G   Bm |
           | C | Bm7 | D | G |
           | G | G | G | G   Bm |
           | C | Bm7 | D | G   G/F♯‖

186

Verse 3

Em   Am
The thing that I tell you now,

D*   G   G/F♯
It may not go over well.

Em   Am
Ah, and it may not be photo-op

D*   G
In the way that I spell it out.

Chorus 3

C   G
But you won't hear from the messenger,

C   D   G   Bm   C
Don't wanna know 'bout some - thing that you don't under - stand.

                     Bm7
You got no fear of the underdog,

D   G   C G D   G C G
That's why you will not sur - vive.   Right.

Outro

C	Bm7	D	G	Bm
C	Bm7	D	G	Bm
C	Bm7	D	G C G D	D G C Gm
C	Bm7	D	G	Bm
C	Bm7	D	G	
G	G	G	G	
G	G	G	G	G

187

To Be Young
(Is To Be Sad, Is To Be High)

Words & Music by
Ryan Adams & David Rawlings

Intro

| G | | G | | C | G | G | | G | | C | G | G | ‖ |

Verse 1

G   C   B♭   G
    Young boy you done me bad I went and did ya wrong
G   C   B♭   G
    Young boy you done me bad I went and did ya wrong.

Chorus 1

          C7   G7
Then I got high, Lord I got high
          D7
Now I got a bone to pick with you
          C7
And I'm sure you know it's true.

Bridge 1

Em   G   C   G G/F♯
    Oh one day when you're looking back
Em   G   C7   G
    You were young and man you were sad
              C7   G
When you're young you get sad,
D7/A   C7   Am   D7 | Dsus4/C | Bm7 |
When you're young you get   sad then you get high.

Link 1

     G | G | C | G | G | G | C | G | G | ‖
Oh man.

Verse 2

G   C   B♭   G
   Young gal I done you bad and I went and did ya wrong,

G   C   B♭   G
Young gal you done me bad so I went and did ya wrong.

Chorus 2

       C7   G7
Then I got high, Lord I got high,

             D7
Now you got a bone to pick with me

       C7
But I wish you'd let me be.

Bridge 2

Em   G   C   G   G/F♯
   Oh one day when you're looking back

Em   G   C7   G
   You were young and man you were sad

         C7   G
When you're young you get sad

         C7   Am   D7 | Dsus4/C | Bm7 |
When you're young you get   sad then you get high,

Dsus4/A D7 | D7/C | Bm7 | D7/A
You get high.

Outro

Gmaj7   C   Em7/B
   Oh the days the rain would fall your way

Gmaj7   C   Em7/B
   Oh the days the rain would fall your way

            Am
Then you'd be   high,

             D7 | D7/C | Bm7 | Dsus4/A
'Cause you got sad

             D7 | D7/C | Bm7 | Dsus4/A
'Cause you got sad

   G   C   G   G   C   G
Oh man,   oh man,

   G   C   G   G   C   Gmaj7*
Oh man,   oh man.

To Ohio

Words & Music by
Benjamin Knox Miller, Jeffrey Prystowsky & Jocelyn Adams

C   F   G

Capo second fret

Intro | C | C | C | C   ‖

Verse 1

C   F   C
I left Louisiana on the rail line, ooh,___
G   F   C
I left Louisiana on the rail line, ooh.___

                                     F   C
Lost my love before her time, ooh,___
G   F   C
Lost my love before her time, ooh.___

        G   F   C
On the way to O - hi - o,
        G   F   C
On the way to O - hi - o.

Instrumental 1 | C | C | F | C |

| G | G | F | C |

| C | C | C   ‖

Verse 2

C   F   C
Every new love is just a shadow, ooh,___
        G   F   C
Yeah, every new love is just a shadow, ooh.___

                                                          F   C
'Cause once you've known love you don't know how to find love, ooh,___
        G   F   C
Yeah, once you've known love you don't know how to find new love.

        G   F   C
All the way to O - hi - o,
        G   F   C
All the way to O - hi - o.

Instrumental 2 | C | C | F | C |

                     | G | G | F | C |

                     | C F | C | C ‖

Verse 3

```
C                                                    F      C
Heard her voice come through the pines of O - hi - o,
  G                                          F      C
I heard her voice singing in the pines of O - hi - o.
                                             F      C
Singing bless your soul, you crossed that line to O - hi - o,
    G                                        F      C
Yeah, bless your soul, you crossed that line to O - hi - o.
      G         F  C
All the way to O - hi - o,
      G         F  C
All the way to O - hi - o,
      G         F  C
All the way to O - hi - o,
      G         F  C
All the way to O - hi - o.
```

Trouble In Mind

Words & Music by
Erland Cooper, Simon Tong & David Nock

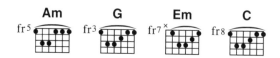

Tune guitar down a semitone

Intro

‖: Am | G | Em | Em :‖

Verse 1

Am   G   Em
  Last night I dreamt when we were young,
Am   G   Em
  Out in the fields I saw you run.
          Am   G   Em
Trouble in mind,   trouble in soul,
          Am G   Em
Won't you let   your feelings go.

Chorus 1

(Em)   Am   C
I didn't mean to dis - appoint you,
         G   Am
I'm just sorry that I had to.
                  C
Didn't mean to dis - appoint you,
         G   Am
I'm just sorry that I did.

Link 1

‖: Am | G | Em | Em :‖

Verse 2

Am   G   Em
  We took a walk down your old   street,
Am   G   Em
  Down past the places we used to meet.
          Am G   Em
Troubled times,   troubled souls,
          Am G   Em
Won't you let   your feelings go.

| *Chorus 2* | As Chorus 1 |

Bridge 1

```
Am              C
La la la la la la la,
     G        Am
La la la la la la la.
             C
La la la la la la la,
     G        Am
La la la la la la la.
Am  C  G  Am
Oh._____
Am  C  G  Am
Oh._____
```

Link 2

‖: Am │ G │ Em │ Em :‖

Verse 3

```
Am              G                    Em
   Your father's house never looked so cold,
Am            G             Em
   What once was new, now over - grown.
         Am  G         Em
Oh pha - raoh,   oh pha - raoh,
            Am  G          Em
Won't you let     your children go.
```

| *Chorus 3* | As Chorus 1 |

Bridge 2

```
Am              C
La la la la la la la,
     G        Am
La la la la la la la.
             C
La la la la la la la,
     G        Am
La la la la la la la.
```

| *Chorus 4* | As Chorus 1 |

Outro

‖: Am │ C │ G │ Am :‖

True Love Will Find You In The End

Words & Music by
Daniel Johnston

D   G   Bm   Em

Intro | D | D | D | D | D | D   ‖

Verse 1

D
True love will find you in the end,
G   D
  You'll find out just who was your friend.
Bm   Em
  Don't be sad, I know you will,
G   D
  But don't give up until true love finds you in the end.

Verse 2

D
This is a promise with a catch,
G   D
  Only if you're looking will it find you.

'Cause true love is searching too,
G
  But how can it recognise you
                   D
Unless you step out into the light, the light?
Bm   Em
  Don't be sad, I know you will,
G   D
  But don't give up until true love finds you in the end.

Instrumental | D | D | D | D |

| G | G | D | D |

| D | D | D | D |

| G | G | D | D |

| Bm | Bm | Em | Em |

| G | G | G | G | D | D   ‖

Verse 3

Bm   Em
   Don't be sad, I know you will,
G   D
   But don't give up until true love finds you in the end,
G   D
   True love will find you in the end.

Outro | G | G | D | D |

| G | G | D   ‖

195

Walkin' Man

Words & Music by
Steve Wold

D   G(add9)/B   D/F♯   D/E

⑥ = D   ③ = F♯
⑤ = A   ② = A
④ = D   ① = D

Intro

‖: D | G(add9)/B | D | G(add9)/B :‖

Verse 1

G(add9)/B D   G(add9)/B   D
You say   jump, I say how high e - xactly do you
G(add9)/B   D   G(add9)/B D G(add9)/B
Want me to jump to,   mmm.
                    D   G(add9)/B   D
And you say walk, I will walk to the end of the
G(add9)/B   D   G(add9)/B D
Line and back to you,   mmm.
                    D/F♯
My name's Steve and I'm your
D/E   D   G(add9)/B   D G(add9)/B
Walkin' man, yes I am.

Verse 2

G(add9)/B D   G(add9)/B   D
You say   boy do you really love me, but   I ain't
G(add9)/B   D   G(add9)/B D   G(add9)/B
Got much words to say,   hey, hey.
                 D   G(add9)/B D
Let me write my answer   down in the
G(add9)/B   D   G(add9)/B D   G(add9)/B
Sand by the waves,   hey, hey.
                   D/F♯
My name's Steve and I'm your
D/E   D   G(add9)/B   D G(add9)/B
Writin' man, yes I am.
                   D/F♯
My name's Steve and I'm your
D/E   D   G(add9)/B   D G(add9)/B
Walkin' man, yes I am.

Instrumental | D | D | D | D |

| D | G(add9)/B | D | G(add9)/B   ‖

Verse 3

G(add9)/B D   G(add9)/B D
If you   want me to stay, I'll   stash my sleeping

G(add9)/B   D   G(add9)/B D   G(add9)/B
Roll under your bed,   hey, hey.

               D   G(add9)/B D
That says more than any - thing   in my

G(add9)/B   D   G(add9)/B D   G(add9)/B
Life I've ever said,   hey, hey.

               D/F♯
My name's Steve and I'm your

D/E   D   G(add9)/B   D G(add9)/B
Stayin' man, yes I am.

               D/F♯
My name's Steve and I'm your

D/E   D   G(add9)/B   D G(add9)/B
Writin' man, yes I am.

               D/F♯
My name's Steve and I'm your

D/E   D
Walkin' man, yes I am.

We Can Be Strong

Words & Music by
Willy Mason

Am   C   F   G

Capo fourth fret

Intro
‖: Am C | F C | F C | Am G :‖

| G | G ‖

Verse 1

Am   F G   Am
  Signed my-self out to - day,

       F   G   Am
I sent a letter far a - way,

      F   G   Am
I said baby I'll be good some - day,

             F G Am   F   G   Am
Gonna try again   to - mor - row, try a - gain to - mor - row.

Verse 2

Am   F   G   Am
  I couldn't take that sterile place,

       F   G   Am
In those rooms I lost my face

          F   G   Am
And in the end they couldn't sell me grace,

             F   G   Am   F   G   Am
And they can't sell me to - mor - row, can't sell me to - mor - row.

Chorus 1

Am   C   F   C   F   C   Am   G
  We can be strong,___ strong,___ strong.___

Am   C   F   C   F   C   Am   G
  We can be strong,___ strong,___ strong.___

Verse 3

```
Am          F      G          Am
  Now I'm back on mamma's couch,
            F      G          Am
Plenty of time to think about
            F            G      Am
All of the kids that went the college route,
          F      G      Am          F      G      Am
Chasing their to - mor - rows, chasing their to - mor - rows.
```

Verse 4

```
Am          F      G              Am
  One by one my friends dropped out,
          F          G        Am
Now I've got brothers to share my doubts
          F              G        Am
On what this   business is all really a - bout,
        F      G      Am          F      G      Am
Waiting on to - mor - row, waiting on to - mor - row.
```

Chorus 2   As Chorus 1

Instrumental   ‖: Am F │ G Am │ Am F │ G Am :‖

Verse 5

```
Am              F  G      Am
  Signed my - self out to - day,
            F    G          Am
I sent a letter far away,
          F          G        Am
I said baby come home to - day,
              F      G      Am                F      G      Am
I'm here and it's to - mor - row, I'm home and it's to - mor - row.
```

Chorus 3

```
Am       C  F    C   F   C   Am   G
  We can be strong,___ strong,___ strong.___
Am       C  F    C   F   C   Am   G
  We can be strong,___ strong,___ strong.___
Am       C  F    C   F   C   Am   G
  We can be strong,___ strong,___ strong.___
Am       C  F    C   F   C   Am   G   Am
  We can be strong,___ strong,___ strong.___
```

We Are The People

Words & Music by
Luke Steele, Nicholas Littlemore & Jonathan Sloan

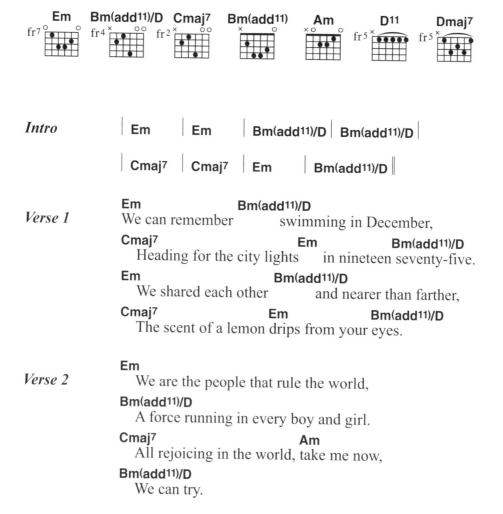

Intro | Em | Em | Bm(add¹¹)/D | Bm(add¹¹)/D |

| Cmaj⁷ | Cmaj⁷ | Em | Bm(add¹¹)/D ‖

Verse 1

Em   Bm(add¹¹)/D
We can remember   swimming in December,
Cmaj⁷   Em   Bm(add¹¹)/D
Heading for the city lights   in nineteen seventy-five.
Em   Bm(add¹¹)/D
We shared each other   and nearer than farther,
Cmaj⁷   Em   Bm(add¹¹)/D
The scent of a lemon drips from your eyes.

Verse 2

Em
We are the people that rule the world,
Bm(add¹¹)/D
A force running in every boy and girl.
Cmaj⁷   Am
All rejoicing in the world, take me now,
Bm(add¹¹)/D
We can try.

Verse 3

Em   Bm(add¹¹)/D
  We lived an adventure,   love in the summer.

Cmaj⁷
  Followed the sun till night,

Am   Bm(add¹¹)/D   Em
Reminiscing other times of life.

                        Bm(add¹¹)/D
For each every other,   the feeling was stronger,

Cmaj⁷   Am   Bm(add¹¹)/D
  The shock hit eleven, we got lost in your eyes.

Chorus 1

  Cmaj⁷   Em
I can't do well when I think you're gonna leave me,

      D¹¹
But I know I try.

            Cmaj⁷   Em
Are you gonna leave me now?

             Dmaj⁷
Can't you be be - lieving now?

  Cmaj⁷   Em
I can't do well when I think you're gonna leave me,

      D¹¹
But I know I try.

            Cmaj⁷   Em
Are you gonna leave me now?

             Dmaj⁷
Can't you be be - lieving now?

Verse 4

Em
  Can you remember the human life,

Bm(add¹¹)/D   Cmaj⁷
  It was still where we'd energize.

                         Am   Bm(add¹¹)/D   Em
Lie in the sand and visualize like it's seventy-five a - gain.

Em
  We are the people that rule the world,

Bm(add¹¹)/D
  A force running in every boy and girl.

Cmaj⁷   Am
  All rejoicing in the world, take me now.

Bm(add¹¹)/D
  We can try.

Chorus 2   As Chorus 1

Bridge

Em   Bm(add11)
I know everything about you,

                       Cmaj7
Know everything about me,

                     Am Bm(add11)
Know everything about us.

Em   Bm(add11)
I know everything about you,

                       Cmaj7
Know everything about me,

                     Am Bm(add11)
Know everything about us.

Chorus 3

‖: Cmaj7   Em
I can't do well when I think you're gonna leave me,

      D11
But I know I try.

                Cmaj7   Em
Are you gonna leave me now?

                Dmaj7
Can't you be be - lieving now? :‖ *Repeat 4 times to fade*

Weekend Wars

Words & Music by
Andrew VanWyngarden & Benjamin Goldwasser

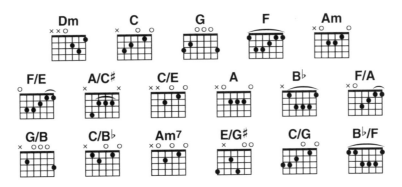

Verse 1

  Dm   C   G
Evil S.I.S to find a shore,

   C   G   F
A beach that doesn't quiver any - more.

    Dm   C   F
And we could crush some plants to paint my walls,

    Am   F
And I won't try to fight in the weekend wars.

Dm   C   G
Was I, I was too lazy to bathe

   C   G   F
Or paint or write or try to make a change?

    Dm   C   F
Now I can shoot a gun to kill my lunch,

    Am   F
And I don't have to love or think too much.

Link 1 | F F/E F | F F/E F F/E ‖

Bridge 1

A/C♯ Dm   C/E   F   A   B♭
      Instant battle plans written on the sidewalk,

A/C♯ Dm   C/E   F   A   B♭
      Mental mystics in a twisted metal car

A/C♯ Dm   C/E   F   B♭   F/A B♭ G/B C   C/B♭ Am7 A/C♯
      Try to ampli - fy the sound of   light and   love.

Verse 2

Dm   C   G
Christ is cursed of fathers and mo - thers,

        C   G   F
Might even take a knife to split a hair.

      Dm   C   F
Or even scare the children off my lawn,

          Am   F
Giving us time to make the makeshift bombs.

Dm   C   G
Every mess invested was a score,

      C   G   F
We couldn't use com - puters any - more.

          Dm   C   F
But it's difficult to win unless you're bored,

              Am   F
And you might have to plan for the weekend wars.

Instrumental | Am | Am | Dm | Dm |

                 | C | C | G | G |

                 | F | F | F | F F/E F |

                 | F F/E F F/E | F F/E F F/E ‖

A/C♯ Dm   C/E   F   A   B♭
Try to break my heart, I'll drive to Ari - zona,

A/C♯ Dm   C/E F   A   B♭
It might take a hundred years to grow an arm.

A/C♯ Dm   C/E F   B♭   F/A B♭ G/B A/C♯
I'll sit and listen to the sound of   sand and cold

Dm   C/E   F   A   B♭
Twisted diamond heart, I'm the weekend warrior.

A/C♯ Dm   C/E   F   A   B♭
My pre - dictions are the only things I have,

A/C♯ Dm C/E   F   B♭   F/A B♭ G/B C   C/B♭ Am7 E/G♯ C/G
I can ampli - fy the sound of   light and love.

    C/G   B♭/F   B♭
‖: I'm a curse and I'm a sound when I open up my mouth,

                       F   C/G
There's a reason I don't win, I don't know how to be - gin. :‖

Repeat to fade

What Would I Want? Sky

Words & Music by
David Portner, Noah Lennox, Brian Weitz, Phil Lesh & Betty Peterson

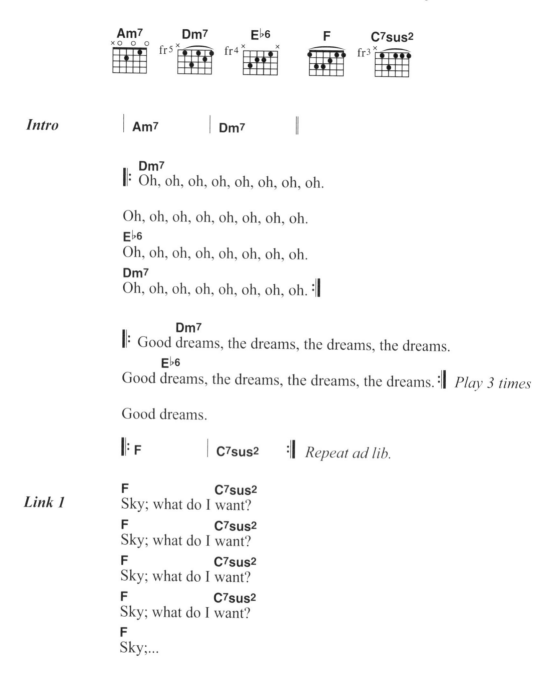

Intro | Am7 | Dm7   ‖

Dm7
‖: Oh, oh, oh, oh, oh, oh, oh, oh.

Oh, oh, oh, oh, oh, oh, oh, oh.
E♭6
Oh, oh, oh, oh, oh, oh, oh, oh.
Dm7
Oh, oh, oh, oh, oh, oh, oh, oh. :‖

                     Dm7
‖: Good dreams, the dreams, the dreams, the dreams.
          E♭6
Good dreams, the dreams, the dreams, the dreams. :‖ *Play 3 times*

Good dreams.

‖: F | C7sus2   :‖ *Repeat ad lib.*

Link 1
F   C7sus2
Sky; what do I want?
F   C7sus2
Sky; what do I want?
F   C7sus2
Sky; what do I want?
F   C7sus2
Sky; what do I want?
F
Sky;...

Verse 1

F   C7sus2 F   C7sus2
Is everything all right?   You feelin' mouldy?

F   C7sus2 F   C7sus2
You feelin' lonely?   You're not the only.

F   C7sus2 F   C7sus2
Is everything all right?   You feelin' stormy?

F   C7sus2 F   C7sus2
You feelin' phony?   You're not the only.

F   C7sus2
Do you get up,   up, up?

F   C7sus2
Clouds stop and move above me,

F   C7sus2   F   C7sus2
Too bad they can't help me, what is the right way?

F   C7sus2   F   C7sus2
Do I float up,   up, up   when I stop and look around me?

F   C7sus2   F   C7sus2
Gray's where that color should be,   what is the right way?

F   C7sus2   F   C7sus2
Old glasses clinking and a   new order's blinking and I,

F   C7sus2   F   C7sus2
I should be floatin', but I'm weighted by thinking.

Chorus 1

        F   E♭6   Dm7
That a guide on the river, really can't make a change,

           F   C7sus2
When the sky gets filled up   too fast

      E♭6   C7sus2
And the taxi man's sayin', you better;

F   C7sus2   E♭6   Dm7
Give him some money, stop   daydreamin' dude.

          F   C7sus2 E♭6   C7sus2
When the thought of hori - zon is hiding from you,

              F
What would you want, sky?

Link 2

C7sus2 F   C7sus2
  Sky;   what do I want?

      F   C7sus2
Sky;   what do I want?

      F   C7sus2
Sky;   what do I want?

      F
Sky;...

Verse 2

F   C⁷sus² F   C⁷sus²
Is everything all right? You feelin' lonely?

F   C⁷sus² F   C⁷sus²
 You feelin' mouldy? You're not the only.

F   C⁷sus² F   C⁷sus²
Is everything all right? You feelin' stoney?

F   C⁷sus² F   C⁷sus²
 You feelin' phony? You're not the only.

F   C⁷sus²
Do you get up, up, up?

F   C⁷sus²
 Clouds stop and move above me,

F   C⁷sus² F   C⁷sus²
Too bad they can't help me, what is the right way?

F   C⁷sus² F   C⁷sus²
Do I float up, up, up when I stop and look around me?

F   C⁷sus²   F   C⁷sus²
 Gray's where that color should be, what is the right way?

F   C⁷sus²   F   C⁷sus²
 Old glasses clinking and a new order's blinking and I,

F   C⁷sus²   F   C⁷sus²
 I should be floatin', but I'm weighted by thinking.

Chorus 2

F   E♭6   Dm⁷
I'm a fly on the river gotta make me some change,

F   C⁷sus²   E♭6 Dm⁷
When the sky gets filled up too fast and the taxi cab's waiting.

F   C⁷sus² E♭6   Dm⁷
You better give him some money, stop daydreaming dude,

F   C⁷sus² E♭6   Dm⁷
When the thought of ho - rizon is hiding it's blues,

F   C⁷sus²
What would you want; sky?

E♭6   Dm⁷   F
 What would I want; sky?

C⁷sus²   E♭6
What would I want; sky?

     Dm⁷   F
𝄆 What would I want; sky?

     C⁷sus² E♭6
What would I want; sky? 𝄇 *Play 6 times*

Outro

   F   C⁷sus²   F
𝄆 What would I want; sky? 𝄇 *Play 5 times*

     C⁷sus²
What would I want?

Grizzly Bear

While You Wait For The Others

Words & Music by
Daniel Rossen, Christopher Bear, Edward Droste & Christopher Taylor

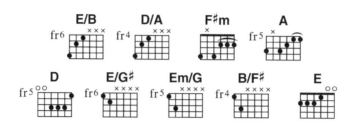

⑥ = D ③ = G
⑤ = A ② = B
④ = D ① = E

Intro | E/B | E/B | E/B | E/B ‖

Verse 1

E/B   D/A   F♯m   A   D A
   While you wait for the others to make it all worthwhile,

E/B   D/A   F♯m   A   D A
   All your useless pre - tensions are weighing on my time.

E/B   D/A   F♯m   A   D A
   You could beg for for - giveness as long as you like,

E/B   D/A
   Or just wait out the evening.

Pre-chorus 1

(D/A) E/G♯ Em/G   B/F♯
You'll only bleed me dry,

        E/G♯ Em/G   B/F♯
Yes, you'll only bleed me dry

    E
So I'll ask you kindly to make your way.

Chorus 1

D   A F♯m A   D
 (Ah,__ oh.____) And what was   left,

   A F♯m A   D
(Ah,__ oh.____) The perfect   cleft,

   A F♯m A   D
(Ah,__ oh.____) We all fall   through.

   A F♯m A
(Ah,__ oh.____)

Verse 2

E/B   D/A   F♯m   A   D A
While you wait on the answers that I'll pretend to find,

E/B   D/A   F♯m   A   D A
Keeping up with e - motions still occupies our time.

E/B   D/A   F♯m   A   D A
You could hope for some substance as long as you like,

E/B   D/A
Or just wait out the evening.

Pre-chorus 2

       E/G♯   Em/G   B/F♯
And always ask me why,

             E/G♯ Em/G   B/F♯
Yes, you'll only bleed me dry

      E
So I'll ask you kindly to make your way.

Chorus 2   As Chorus 1

Bridge

(A)   A   F♯m   A
And all we want, want, want, want, want, want, want,

       D   A   F♯m   A
Want,__ want, want, want, want, want, want,

       D   A   F♯m   A
Want,__ want,__ want,___ want,__

       D   A   F♯m   A
Want,__ want,__ want,___ want.__

     D A F♯m A
Oh._____

     D A F♯m A
Oh._____

Chorus 3

D   A F♯m A   D
   (Ah,__ oh.____) And what was   left.

    A F♯m A   D
(Ah,__ oh.____) And what was   left.

    A F♯m A   D
(Ah,__ oh.____) And what was   left.

     A F♯m A   D
Ah,__ oh._____

     A F♯m A   D
Ah,__ oh._____

     A F♯m A   D
Ah,__ oh._____

     A F♯m A
Ah,__ oh._____

White Winter Hymnal

Words & Music by
Robin Pecknold

E   F#m   A   B7

Intro

N.C.(E)
I was following the, I was following the,

I was following the, I was following the,

I was following the, I was following the,

I was following the, I was following the,

Verse 1

E
I was following the pack, all swallowed in their coats,

F#m
With scarves of red tied 'round their throats,

To keep their little heads from falling in the snow.

A
And I turned 'round and there you go,

B7
And, Michael, you would fall and turn the white snow red,

(E)
As strawberries in the summertime.

Link 1

| E | E | E | E | |
| A | A | E | E | |

Verse 2   As Verse 1

Instr.

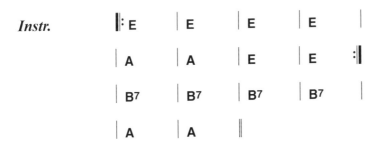

Verse 3

N.C.(E)
I was following the pack, all swallowed in their coats,
(F♯m)
With scarves of red tied 'round their throats,

To keep their little heads from falling in the snow.
(A)
And I turned 'round and there you go,
(B7)
And, Michael, you would fall and turn the white snow red,
(E)
As strawberries in the summertime.

Winter Winds

Words & Music by
Mumford & Sons

C   G   G/B   D   C/G   Em

Intro

| C | G | C G/B | D | D | |

| C | G | C G/B | D | |

| G C/G | G C/G | G C/G | G | ||

Verse 1

G   D   C
As the winter winds litter London with lonely hearts,

          G   D   Em   C
Oh, the warmth in your eyes swept me into your arms.

          G   D   Em   C
Was it love or fear of the cold that lead us through the night?

        G   D   Em   C
For every kiss your beauty trumped my doubt.

Chorus 1

C   G   C G/B D
And my head told my heart: "Let love grow,"

       C   G   C G/B D   G C/G G C/G G C/G
But my heart told my head: "This time no, this time no."

Verse 2

G   D   Em   C
We'll be washed and buried one day my girl

          G   D   Em   C
And the time we were given will be left for the world.

        G   D   Em   C
The flesh that lived and loved will be eaten by plague,

        G   D   Em   C
So let the memo - ries be good for those who stay, hey.

Chorus 2

```
      N.C.    C          G             C  G/B  D
      And my head told my heart: "Let love grow,"
              C          G          C   G/B  D
      But my heart told my head: "This time no."
                C          G         C   G/B  D                   G C/G  G C/G  G C/G  G
      Yes, my heart told my head: "This time no, this time no."
```

Verse 3

```
      G                           D          Em            C
      Oh, the shame that sent me off from the God that I once loved
              G              D      C
      Was the same that sent me into your arms.
              G           D             Em         C
      Oh, and pestilence is won when you are lost and I am gone
              G        D               C
      And no hope, no hope will over - come.
           G      D          Em    C
      But if your strife strikes at your sleep,
           G        D           Em       C
      Re - member spring swaps snow for leaves.
      G         D        Em            C
      You'll be happy and wholesome a - gain
                 G   D        Em     C
      When the city clears and sun as - cends, hey.
```

Instrumental

```
| N.C. C | G      | C G/B | D      | D      |
| C      | G      | C G/B | D      | D      ‖
```

Chorus 3

```
      D      C         G             C  G/B  D
      And my head told my heart: "Let love grow,"
              C          G          C   G/B  D
      But my heart told my head: "This time no."
                C          G         C   G/B  D
      And my head told my heart: "Let love grow,"
              C          G          C   G/B  D              C
      But my heart told my head: "This time no, this time no."
                G
      Oh._____
```

You And I

Words & Music by
Jeff Tweedy

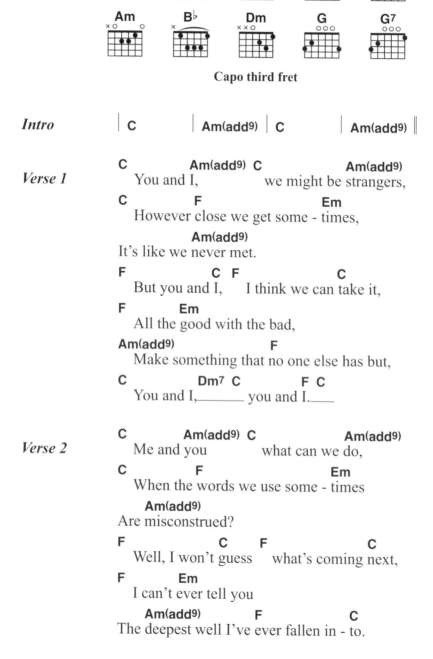

Capo third fret

Intro | C | Am(add9) | C | Am(add9) ‖

Verse 1
C   Am(add9) C   Am(add9)
You and I,   we might be strangers,
C   F   Em
However close we get some - times,
        Am(add9)
It's like we never met.
F   C F   C
But you and I,   I think we can take it,
F   Em
All the good with the bad,
Am(add9)   F
Make something that no one else has but,
C   Dm7 C   F C
You and I,_____ you and I.____

Verse 2
C   Am(add9) C   Am(add9)
Me and you   what can we do,
C   F   Em
When the words we use some - times
        Am(add9)
Are misconstrued?
F   C F   C
Well, I won't guess what's coming next,
F   Em
I can't ever tell you
        Am(add9)   F   C
The deepest well I've ever fallen in - to.

Link | C | Am(add9) | C | Am(add9) ‖

Bridge

    F   Em
    Oh, I don't wanna know,   oh, I don't wanna know,

    C   Am
    Oh, I don't need to know everything about you.

    F
    Oh, I don't wanna know

        C   Bb   Am   Dm   G G7
And you don't need to know that much about me

Verse 3

    C   Am(add9) C   Am(add9)
    You and I,   we might be strangers,

    C   F   Em
    However close we get some - times,

          Am(add9)
It's like we never met.

    F   C F   C
    But you and I,   I think we can take it,

    F   Em
    All the good with the bad,

Am(add9)   F
    Make something that no one else has but,

    C   Dm7 C   F C
    You and I,_____ you and I.____

          Dm7 C   F C
You and I,_____ you and I.____

          Dm7 C   F C
You and I,_____ you and I.____

          Dm7 C   F C
You and I,_____ you and I.____

Outro   ‖: C | Dm7 | C | F   :‖ *Repeat to fade*

Young Bride

Words & Music by
Tim Smith

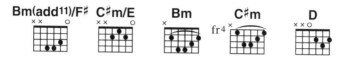

Tune guitar down a semitone

Intro 　‖: Bm(add11)/F♯ | C♯m/E 　　:‖ *Play 8 times*

Verse 1

Bm(add11)/F♯ C♯m/E
　　My young bride,

　　　　　　Bm(add11)/F♯ C♯m/E　　　　Bm(add11)/F♯
Why are your shoulders like that of a tired old woman?

C♯m/E　　　　　Bm(add11)/F♯ C♯m/E
　Like a tired old woman.

Bm(add11)/F♯ C♯m/E
　　My young bride,

　　　　　　　　　C♯m/E　　　Bm(add11)/F♯
Why are your fingers like that of the hedge in winter?

C♯m/E　　　　　Bm(add11)/F♯ C♯m/E
　Of the hedge in winter.

Chorus 1

Bm　　　　C♯m　Bm　　　　C♯m
Polo - naise in winter, snowshoes and hunters,

Bm　　C♯m　　　Bm C♯m
Carry the goods in for you.

Link　　| Bm　　　| C♯m　　| Bm　　　| C♯m　　‖

Verse 2

Bm   C♯m
   My young bride,

     Bm   C♯m   Bm
Why aren't you moving at all, helps to make the day seem shorter.

C♯m   Bm   C♯m
  Helps to make the day seem shorter.

Bm   C♯m
  My young bride,

     Bm   C♯m   Bm
Why aren't you keeping with you all the ones who really love you?

C♯m   Bm   C♯m
  All the ones who really love you.

Chorus 2

Bm   C♯m   Bm   C♯m
Polo - naise in winter, snowshoes and hunters,

Bm   C♯m   Bm C♯m
Carry the goods in for you.

Bm   C♯m D   C♯m
Darkness and forest grant you the longest

Bm   C♯m   Bm C♯m
Face made from porridge and stew.

Instrumental ‖: Bm | C♯m | Bm | C♯m   :‖

Chorus 3   As Chorus 2

Chorus 4   As Chorus 2

Chorus 5   As Chorus 2 *Fade out*

Your Protector

Words & Music by
Robin Pecknold

Em   D   C   A   G   Am   Bm   Cmaj7

Intro

| (Em) | (Em) | (Em) | (Em) |

| (C) | (C) (D) | (Em) | (Em) ||

Verse 1

(Em)   (D)   (Em)
She left a week to roam, your pro - tector's coming home
        (C)   (D)   (Em)
Keep your secrets with you girl, safe from the out - side world.
                                            (D)   (Em)
You walk along the stream, your head caught in a waking dream,
        (C)   (D)   (Em)
Your pro - tector's coming home, coming home

Chorus 1

(Em)   C
As you lay to die beside me, baby,
        G   D
On the morning that you came,
            Em   A
Would you wait for me,
        G   A   Em
The other one would wait for me.
            C
As you lay to die beside me, baby,
        G   D
On the morning that you came,
            Em   A
Would you wait for me,
        G   A   Em
The other one would wait for me.

Link | (Em) | (Em) | (Em) | (Em) ||

Bridge

Em
You run with the devil.

You run with the devil.

Ooh, ooh, ooh, ooh.

Ooh, ooh, ooh, ooh.

Tell your brother to be good,
        Am   **Em**
Tell your sister not to   go,

Tell your mother not to wait,
        Am   **Em**
Tell your father I was   good.

Chorus 2

(Em)   C
As you lay to die beside me, baby,
        G   **D**
On the morning that you came,
           Em   **A**
Would you wait for me,
    G   **A**   **Em**
The other one would wait for me.

Outro

Em   A   G   A Em A   G A Bm
Ooh,____ ooh,____ ooh,____ ooh.____
Cmaj⁷ Bm   Cmaj⁷ Bm Cmaj⁷ Bm G   A Em
Ooh,____ ooh,____ ooh,____ ooh.____
Em   A   G   A Em A   G A Bm
Ooh,____ ooh,____ ooh,____ ooh.____
Cmaj⁷ Bm   Cmaj⁷ Bm Cmaj⁷ Bm G   A Em
Ooh,____ ooh,____ ooh,____ ooh.____

Your Rocky Spine

Words & Music by
Tony Dekker

Capo fifth fret

Intro

‖: Dm | C | G7 | B♭ :‖

Verse 1

(B♭) Dm   C
I was lost in the lakes
          G7   B♭
And the shapes that your body makes,
              Dm   C
That your body makes, that your body makes,
          G7   B♭
That your body makes.

Link 1

| C | B♭ | C | B♭ ‖

Verse 2

(B♭)   Dm   C
And the mountains said I could find you here,
          G7   B♭
They whisper the snow and the leaves in my ear.
        Dm   C
I traced my finger a - long your trails,
          G7   B♭   C
Your body was the map, I was lost in it.

Chorus 1

F   C
Floating over your rocky spine,
          G7   B♭   C
The glaciers made you and now you're mine.
F   C
Floating over your rocky spine,
          G7   B♭   C
The glaciers made you and now you're mine.

Instrumental   ‖: Dm | C | G7 | B♭   :‖

Verse 3

(B♭)   Dm   C
I was moving across your frozen veneer,
      G7   B♭
The sky was dark, but you were clear.
Dm   C
Could you feel my footsteps
                        G7
And would you shatter, would you shatter,
            B♭
Would you?

Link 1 | C | B♭ | C | B♭   ‖

Verse 4

(B♭)   Dm   C
And with your soft fingers be - tween my claws
      G7   B♭
Like purity a - gainst resolve,
            Dm   C
I could tell then there we were formed from the clay
      G7   B♭   C
And came from the rocks for the earth to dis - play.

Chorus 2

(C)   F   C
They told me to be careful up there
                  G7   B♭   C
Where the wind throws a venomous rage through your hair.
            F   C
They told me to be careful up there
                  G7   B♭   C
Where the wind rages through your hair.

Outro   ‖: Dm | C | G7 | B♭   :‖ B♭   ‖

Relative Tuning

The guitar can be tuned with the aid of pitch pipes or dedicated electronic guitar tuners which are available through your local music dealer. If you do not have a tuning device, you can use relative tuning. Estimate the pitch of the 6th string as near as possible to E or at least a comfortable pitch (not too high, as you might break other strings in tuning up). Then, while checking the various positions on the diagram, place a finger from your left hand on the:

5th fret of the E or 6th string and **tune the open A** (or 5th string) to the note (A)

5th fret of the A or 5th string and **tune the open D** (or 4th string) to the note (D)

5th fret of the D or 4th string and **tune the open G** (or 3rd string) to the note (G)

4th fret of the G or 3rd string and **tune the open B** (or 2nd string) to the note (B)

5th fret of the B or 2nd string and **tune the open E** (or 1st string) to the note (E)

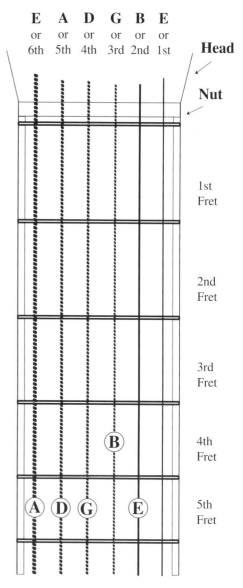

Reading Chord Boxes

Chord boxes are diagrams of the guitar neck viewed head upwards, face on as illustrated. The top horizontal line is the nut, unless a higher fret number is indicated, the others are the frets.

The vertical lines are the strings, starting from E (or 6th) on the left to E (or 1st) on the right.

The black dots indicate where to place your fingers.

Strings marked with an O are played open, not fretted. Strings marked with an X should not be played.

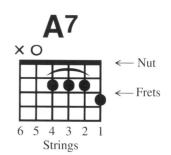

The curved bracket indicates a 'barre' - hold down the strings under the bracket with your first finger, using your other fingers to fret the remaining notes.